PHYSICS *first*

George Bethell
David Coppock

OXFORD
UNIVERSITY PRESS

Oxford University Press, Great Clarendon Street, Oxford OX2 6DP

Oxford New York
Athens Auckland Bangkok Bogota Buenos Aires
Calcutta Cape Town Chennai Dar es Salaam
Delhi Florence Hong Kong Istanbul Karachi
Kuala Lumpur Madrid Melbourne Mexico City
Mumbai Nairobi Paris São Paulo Singapore
Taipei Tokyo Toronto Warsaw

and associated companies in
Berlin Ibadan

Oxford is a registered trade mark of Oxford University Press

© George Bethell, David Coppock 1999

The moral rights of the author have been asserted.

First published in 1999

British Library Cataloguing in Publication Data
Data available

ISBN 0 19 914733 7

Typeset by Ian Foulis and Associates, Plymouth, Devon
Printed in China

Acknowledgements

The publishers would like to thank the following for providing photographs:

6 **British Airways**, 10 **Chris Honeywell**, 11 **Shell**, 16 (top left) **FLPA/ J. Zimmerman**, 16 (top right) **The Stock Market**, 16 (bottom left) **SPL/ Keith Kent**, 16 (bottom right) **SPL/ John Foster**, 20 **SPL/ NASA**, 21 **Mike Roberts**, 22 (top and bottom) **Peter Gould**, 25 (left) **British Drag Racing Association**, 25 (right) **Colorsport**, 26 (left) **SPL/ Bruce Iverson**, 26 (top right) **SPL/ Tek Image**, 26 (bottom right) **OSF/ David Cayless**, 34 (top left) **Holt Studios**, 34 (top centre) **Colorsport**, 34 (top right) **SPL/ Lerosey, Jerrican**, 34 (bottom left) **SPL/ NASA**, 34 (bottom centre) **Peter Gould**, 34 (bottom right) **OUP picture library**, 39 **Shell**, 40 **Shell**, 45 **Zefa/ J. Pfaff**, 46 (left) **FLPA/ E. & D. Hosking**, 46 (right) **SPL/ Marcelo Brodsky/ Latin Stock**, 47 **Casio Electronics**, 50 **Peter Gould**, 51 **SPL/ Kent Wood**, 55 **Peter Gould**, 57 **Peter Gould**, 58 **Peter Gould**, 61 **Peter Gould**, 63 **Peter Gould**, 65 **Peter Gould**, 68 (both) **Peter Gould**, 74 (top left) **Zefa**, 74 (top right) **Zefa**, 74 (bottom left) **Zefa**, 74 (bottom right) **Argos**, 78 **Zefa**, 79 (left) **Sally and Richard Greenhill**, 79 (centre) **The Hutchison Library/ Robert Francis**, 79 (right) **Sally and Richard Greenhill**, 80 **Sally and Richard Greenhill**, 83 **Chris Honeywell**, 85 **Robert Harding Picture Library**, 87 **Chris Honeywell**, 88 (top) **SPL/ Andrew McClenaghan**, 88 (bottom) **Chris Honeywell**, 92 (left) **Argos**, 92 (centre) **Argos**, 92 (top right) **Argos**, 92 (bottom right) **Chris Honeywell**, 97 (top) **Zefa**, 97 (bottom) **Chris Honeywell**, 100 **Chris Honeywell**, 102 **Chris Honeywell**, 104 **SPL/ NASA**, 108 **Zefa**, 110 **Chris Honeywell**, 111 **SPL/ Martin Dohrin**, 112 **SPL/ European Space Agency**, 116 (right) **Natural History Museum/ Martin Poulsford**, 116 (left) **Peter Gould**, 117 (left) **Natural History Museum/ Martin Poulsford**, 117 (right) **Peter Gould**, 118 (top) **Aspect Picture Library**, 118 (bottom) **Picturepoint**, 119 **Peter Gould**, 121 (left) **Zefa/ J. Pfaff**, 121 (right) **Peter Gould**, 122 (top) **J. Allan Cash**, 122 (bottom) **J. Allan Cash**, 123 **Rex Features/ YoshiaKi Nagashima-PPS**.

The artwork is by: Brian Beckett, Elitta Fell, Ian Foulis & Associates, David La Grange, Nick Hawken, Oxford Illustrators, Jones Sewell, Alan Rowe, Julie Tolliday, and Galina Zolfaghari.

Introduction

Physics is the study of the physical world around us. It covers everything from the nature of the tiny particles that make up atoms, to the laws which control the galaxies as they move through the universe. This huge scale makes physics exciting, but it is also a very practical subject. As you will see, modern technologies such as electronics, information technology and space travel, are all based on applications of physics.

This book has been written for students, like you, studying physics in secondary schools. It covers all the physical processes that you need for Key Stage 3 of the National Curriculum. However, in many places it goes into much greater depth, helping you to develop the kind of understanding needed to gain the highest grades in your SATs. It will also provide a solid foundation if you are preparing for GCSE.

There are nine chapters covering many important topics, particularly those that affect us in our everyday lives. Topics are presented over two or four pages, and there are lots of diagrams and photographs to help you. There are also questions and activities to check that you have understood the main ideas. Each chapter finishes with a page of questions to help you test your knowledge and to prepare for examinations. Of course, physics is more than just learning from books, however good they are, and your school's programme of practical work will help you to develop important experimental skills.

To get the most out of this book:

- use the contents page to find out where the major topics are covered;
- use the index to find the pages where you can read about particular key words;
- use the questions within a chapter to test your knowledge as you go;
- carry out the activities suggested to reinforce your understanding;
- use the questions at the end of each chapter to prepare for tests and examinations.

We hope that you will enjoy using this book and finish it feeling confident that you can use the ideas and methods of physics to understand the way our world works.

George Bethell

David Coppock

Contents

What is a 'force'?
What effects do forces have on materials and moving objects?
How do objects balance?
What is 'pressure' and how do we use it?

A force is a 'push' or a 'pull'. We need to understand forces because they affect all the objects around us. Some forces only act when two objects are touching. These are called **contact forces**. Some forces act **at a distance**, for example the gravitational pull of the Earth holds the Moon in orbit at a distance of over 350 000 km!

All the pieces of metal and concrete in this bridge are acted upon by forces. This changes their shapes. Some pieces are in **tension**: the forces are stretching them. Other pieces are being **compressed**: the forces are squashing them. The weight of the bridge makes it bend in the middle.

A suspension bridge is constructed to utilize forces.

Tension causes stretching.

Compression makes the material shorter.

Bending is caused by forces acting in opposite directions.

Forces change the speed of objects

Forces make things start to move. They also increase or decrease the object's speed. For example, a plane at rest on the runway will not start to move until its engines exert a force. Once it is moving, the force makes the plane accelerate. On landing, the plane has to exert a force in the opposite direction to make it slow down and stop.

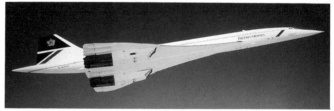

The force from a plane's engines keeps it moving.

Forces change the direction of moving objects

Moving objects tend to move in straight lines. They only change direction when a force acts. For example, a snooker ball moves in a straight line until it hits the 'cushion' at the edge of the table. When the ball meets the cushion, a force makes it bounce off in a different direction.

The cue hitting the ball and the ball hitting the cushion are examples of **contact forces**.

Snooker gives an example of contact forces.

Elasticity and springs

The unit of force

We measure force in units called **newtons (N)**. These are named after the famous physicist Sir Isaac Newton. (It may help you to remember that it takes a force of about 1 N to lift a medium-sized apple!) We can measure a force using a spring balance or **newton meter**.

Elastic materials

Forces can cause materials to stretch. When the forces are removed, the material may spring back to its original length. We call this **elasticity**. For example, a rubber band can be stretched to several times its length but it will still go back to its original size. Rubber is a very elastic material.

Metal wires will also stretch and spring back into shape if the forces are small. However, if the forces are too large, the wire will be left permanently stretched. This happens when we go beyond the material's **elastic limit**.

Springs

Springs are very useful because they stretch evenly when forces are applied. In the graph, the metal spring stretches 10 mm for every 1 N of force added. The graph goes up evenly for 1 N, 2 N, 3 N and 4 N. If we add more than 4 N, the spring still stretches but it does not follow the same pattern.

Robert Hooke (1635–1703) was an English scientist who investigated elasticity. He found that many materials (and springs) extend evenly when stretched by forces – provided that you don't add too much weight. This is known as **Hooke's law**.

Example: forces on a spring

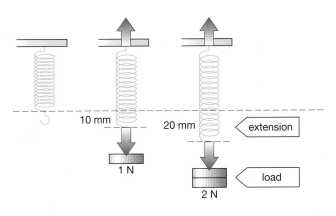

Load in N	0	1	2	3	4	5
Extension in mm	0	10	20	30	40	58

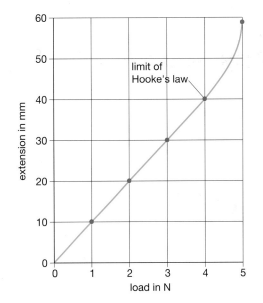

Graph showing the extension of a spring. Materials that stretch evenly obey Hooke's law.

Questions

1   What is meant by:
   a) elastic limit
   b) extension?

2   Why is rubber a good material for:
   a) making 'elastic' bands
   b) making bicycle tyres?

3   A spring stretches by 10 cm when a force of 20 N is applied. When a force of 22 N is used, the spring stretches by 11 cm.
   a) What would be the extension for forces of:
   i) 10 N   ii) 1 N   iii) 15 N?
   b) Can you predict the extension for a force of 30 N acting on this spring? Explain.

More about springs

Springs in series

We saw that, provided we do not use too much force, springs stretch evenly as bigger loads are added. The spring opposite stretches by 20 mm for every 1 N of force applied.

Now what happens if we add another identical spring to the bottom of the first?

When we add 1 N to this arrangement, both springs stretch. They are each acted on by a force of 1 N so they **each** stretch by 20 mm. The total extension is 40 mm. For the same load we get twice the extension.

Springs joined end to end are easier to stretch: for the same force we get a greater extension.

Springs in parallel

We can join two identical springs so that they are side by side. We say that they are **in parallel**.

Now when we add a force of 1 N, the springs can share the load. Each spring is acted upon by 0.5 N, so each spring stretches just 10 mm. Because they are side by side, the total extension is just 10 mm.

Springs joined side by side are harder to stretch: for the same force we get a smaller extension.

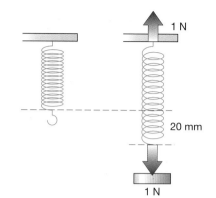

This spring stretches 20 mm when a load of 1N is added.

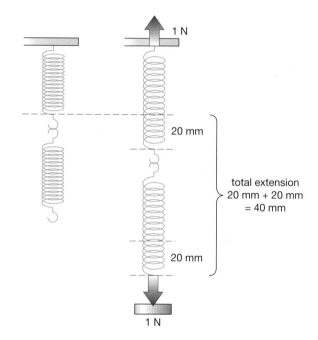

These two springs, joined end to end, stretch 40 mm when a load of 1N is added.

Questions

1   A spring is 80 mm long. It stretches 12 mm when a load of 1 N is applied. How long will the spring be when a load of 2 N hangs from it?

2   A machine in a factory makes wire coils. It cuts the coil to make springs which are 10 cm long. These stretch 1 cm for every 10 N applied. What difference does it make if the machine is set to cut the coil into springs which are:
   a) 5 cm long
   b) 20 cm long?

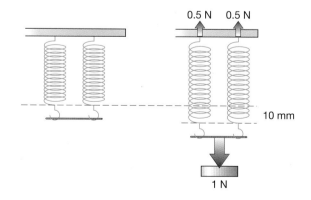

These two springs, joined side by side, stretch 10 mm only when a load of 1 N is added.

Mass, weight, and gravity

Over 300 years ago **Sir Isaac Newton** came up with the idea that all masses attract all other masses. He called this attraction **gravity**. The Earth has a mass of about six million million million million kilograms so its gravitational pull is large and easily measured. Newton's genius helped him to see that it is gravity which pulls an apple to the ground when it falls from a tree, and that it is the same gravity which keeps the planets in their orbits around the Sun.

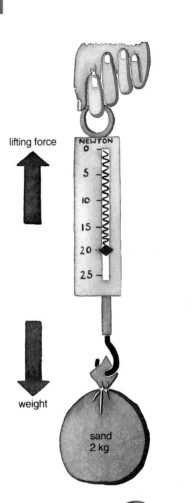

Gravity and weight

When we lift a bag of sand from the ground we have to use a force. This is because the Earth's gravity is pulling downwards with a force. We call this force **weight** and we can measure it with a spring balance or newton meter. Because weight is a force it is measured in newtons. The **mass** which is being acted on by gravity is measured in kilograms. The weight of a 1 kg mass depends on the strength of gravity where the weight is measured.

This might seem confusing but it is easy to understand if you think about taking a 1 kg bag of sugar on a very long journey. In the UK the strength of the gravitational field is about 10 N/kg. This means that it gives a force of 10 N on every kilogram. The Moon is much less massive than the Earth – the strength of the Moon's gravitational field is about 1.6 N/kg.

An astronaut buys a 1 kg bag of sugar in London. Its mass is 1 kg. Its weight is 10 N. She takes the sugar to the Moon without opening it on the way, so its mass is still 1 kg. On the Moon it only weighs 1.6 N!

Working out weight

We know that things with a great mass are difficult to lift. This is because the gravitational force (weight) is large. Since the strength of gravity is the force on each kilogram we just multiply the mass and the field strength to get the weight.

weight = mass × gravity = $m \times g$

Example

An exploration robot of mass 100 kg is built on Earth at a place where the strength of gravity is 9.8 N/kg. It is sent to Mars where the strength of gravity is 3.7 N/kg. What does the robot weigh on Earth and on Mars?

a) Mass on Earth = 100 kg
Strength of gravity on Earth = 9.8 kg/N
Weight on Earth = mass × gravity
= 100 × 9.8 N = **980 N**

b) Mass on Mars = same as on Earth = 100 kg
Strength of gravity on Mars = 3.7 kg/N
Weight on Mars = mass × gravity
= 100 × 3.7 N = **370 N**

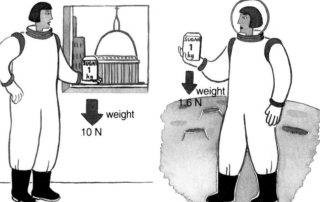

In London 1 kg weighs 10 N.   *On the Moon 1 kg weighs 1.6 N.*

Activities

1 Using bathroom scales find your mass in kilograms. Use your result to calculate what your weight would be **a)** in Paris ($g = 9.8$ N/kg) **b)** at the North Pole ($g = 9.85$ N/kg) **c)** on the Moon ($g = 1.6$ N/kg) **d)** on Mars ($g = 3.7$ N/kg).

2 People who want to get slimmer may go to a club called 'Weight Watchers'. Explain why scientists might argue that it should be called '**Mass** Watchers'!

Kitchen scales balance when the weights on each side are the same. If there is more weight in the left-hand pan then that side moves down. This is because the larger force has a bigger turning effect about the pivot.

The turning effect of a force is called its **moment**.

The scales balance when the forces on each side are equal.

The moment of a force depends on how big the force is. It also depends on the distance of the force from the pivot or fulcrum. The diagram below shows how a large force can be balanced by a smaller force. Notice that the smaller force is further away from the pivot. This increases its turning effect.

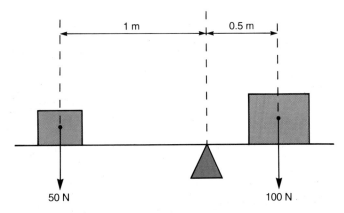

The moment of the force on the left-hand side is 50 N × 1 m = 50 Nm.
The moment of the force on the right-hand side is 100 N × 0.5 m = 50 Nm.
These balance.

Using moments

People have known how to use the moment of a force to do work for thousands of years. For example, the Egyptians used levers and other simple machines to move heavy blocks of stone to make the pyramids

about 50 000 years ago. The diagram below shows how a small force at the end of a long lever can overcome a large force close to the pivot.

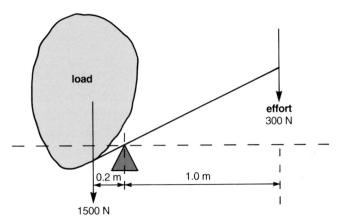

A long lever can enable a small effort to raise a large load.

The lever acts as a **force multiplier** but does not do more **work** than the effort puts in. The effort (300 N) moves through a large distance but the load (1500 N) is only raised by a small amount. In real life, the effort would need to be a bit bigger than 300 N to overcome friction at the pivot.

Useful levers

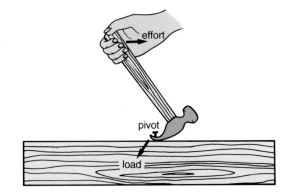

A small effort applied to the end of a hammer can overcome the force holding the nail in the wood.

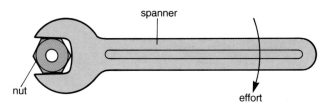

A long-handled spanner allows a small effort to overcome the large forces holding the nut on.

Balance and stability

A metre rule will balance if it is supported at its mid-point. This is because the weights of all the particles on one side of the pivot are balanced by the weights of all the particles on the other side. To the person supporting the rule it is as though all the weight is acting at one point. This point is called the **centre of gravity** (or the **centre of mass**).

For uniform objects like metre rules and billiard balls the centre of gravity is where you would expect – right in the centre! For other shapes you may have to carry out a simple investigation to find it.

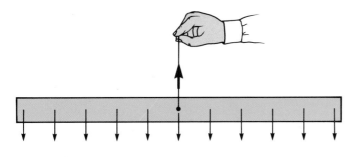

The weights of all the particles to the left of the centre of gravity balance those on the right.

Activities

1 Cut a shape out of a thick piece of card. Punch holes near to two corners.

Now hang the card from a nail or pin as shown in the diagram below.

Use a plumb line to mark a vertical line.

Repeat this with the card suspended from the other corner. Where the two lines cross is the centre of gravity.

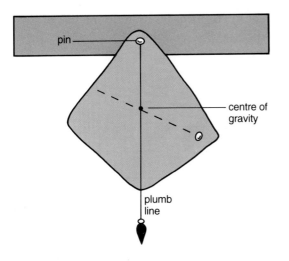

Stability

Some things fall over easily when pushed. They are **unstable**. Others are very difficult to topple. We say that these are **stable**.

The stability of an object depends on how far we can tip it before its weight moves outside its base. When this happens the moment of the weight tips it over.

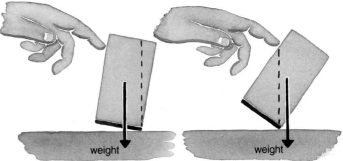

With a small push the weight will tip the box back to its original position.

With a larger push the weight is outside the base and so tips the box over.

Things with wide bases and low centres of gravity are most stable. Designers use this to make their products safer. For example, the Bunsen burners used in a laboratory have a wide, heavy base. This makes them very stable.

Racing cars have low centres of gravity and wide wheelbases.

Activities

1 Draw, in section, these pieces of laboratory equipment: beaker, test tube, conical flask, evaporating dish, measuring cylinder.

Try to get the proportions right.

Comment on the stability of each one.

Pressure

The effect that a force has when it acts on a surface depends on two things: the size of the force and the area that it is pressing on. We measure this as **pressure**.

Pressure is calculated using this equation:

$$\text{pressure} = \frac{\text{force}}{\text{area}}$$

The unit of pressure is the **pascal (Pa)**. When 1 N of force acts on an area of 1 m^2, we say there is a pressure of 1 pascal.

The high heel on this shoe causes a lot of damage to the floor. The force acts on a very small area. The pressure is very high!

Examples

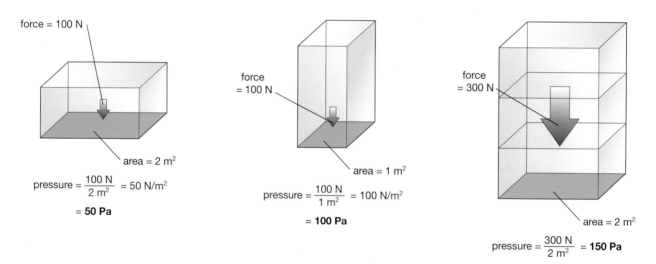

force = 100 N

area = 2 m^2

$$\text{pressure} = \frac{100\ \text{N}}{2\ \text{m}^2} = 50\ \text{N/m}^2$$

$$= \mathbf{50\ Pa}$$

force = 100 N

area = 1 m^2

$$\text{pressure} = \frac{100\ \text{N}}{1\ \text{m}^2} = 100\ \text{N/m}^2$$

$$= \mathbf{100\ Pa}$$

force = 300 N

area = 2 m^2

$$\text{pressure} = \frac{300\ \text{N}}{2\ \text{m}^2} = \mathbf{150\ Pa}$$

This block exerts a pressure of 50 Pa.

The pressure is now 100 Pa because the same force is pressing on a smaller area.

The pressure here is 150 Pa. The force is three times bigger than with just one block.

Using high pressure

Reduce the area so that the force is more concentrated. This makes the object cut more deeply into the surface. Examples include sharp knives, drawing pins, and ice skates.

Hockey boots

The force acts on the small area of the stud. The high pressure makes the stud sink into the ground.

Using low pressure

Increase the area so the force is more spread out. This stops the object sinking so deeply into the surface. Other examples include the use of skis and snow-shoes.

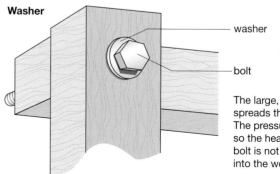

Washer

washer

bolt

The large, flat washer spreads the force. The pressure is small so the head of the bolt is not pulled into the wood.

Pressure in liquids

Pressure in liquids

When you pour a liquid into a container, its weight pushes down on the container's base. The **pressure** on the base is given by the force (**weight**) divided by the area it acts on.

$$\text{pressure} = \frac{\text{force}}{\text{area}}$$

The unit of pressure is the **pascal** (**Pa**).

The pressure in the liquid is not the same at all depths. It is small just under the surface but increases as you go deeper. This can be shown by drilling small holes in the container as shown in the diagram opposite. The top jet does not travel as far as the jets from the holes below because the pressure is not so large. Notice that the direction of the pressure causing the jets of liquid is outwards. In fact, **pressure at any point in a liquid acts equally in all directions**.

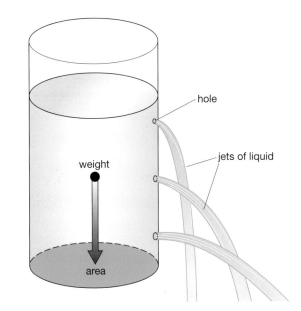

Pressure in a liquid increases with depth.

Density affects pressure

The density of the liquid also affects the pressure. Dense liquids have a greater weight for the same volume so they press down on the container with greater pressure. The diagram compares the pressure at the bottom of a beaker of water with the pressure at the bottom of a beaker of the liquid metal mercury.

Container shape doesn't affect pressure

It may seem surprising but the pressure in a liquid **does not** depend on the shape of the container. The diagram below shows four different 'containers' joined together. When you pour in a liquid it rises to the same level in each section. This proves that the pressures at points A, B, C, and D are the same.

Questions

1   Why do submarines need thick, strong walls?

2   A tank for storing liquid has a base of area 1.5 m². What is the pressure on the base of the tank when it contains:
   a) water weighing 6000 N
   b) oil weighing 4500 N?

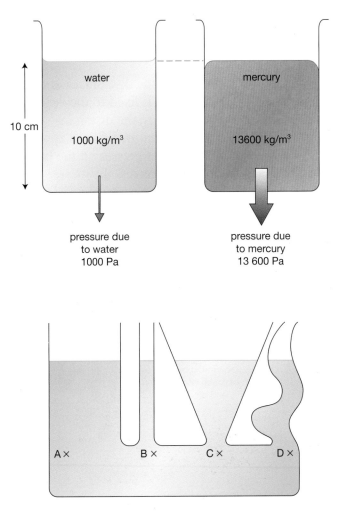

Liquid rises to the same level in each section of 'Pascal's vases'.

Hydraulic machines

Liquids are very difficult to compress because their particles are very close together. If you apply a force to the surface of a liquid which is trapped inside a container, then the pressure is transmitted throughout the liquid. You can use this fact to build machines which use **hydraulic pressure** to move pistons inside cylinders.

Lifting heavy loads

The diagram opposite shows a simple hydraulic jack used to lift heavy loads. Here a force of 200 N pushes down on a small piston in the **master cylinder**. The pressure on the oil is 2000 Pa. The oil transmits this so that it pushes on the larger cylinder in the **slave cylinder**. Now the 2000 Pa is pressing on a bigger area so it can lift a larger load (force). In this machine the pressure pushes on an area which is 5 times bigger. So the force that can be lifted is 5 times bigger. An effort of 200 N can lift a load of 1000 N. The jack acts as a **force multiplier**.

Braking forces

Hydraulic forces are used in the disc brakes of cars and motor bikes. A steel disc is fixed to the centre of each wheel. As the wheel turns, the disc spins between two brake pads. When the brake is applied, a piston in the master cylinder presses on the **brake fluid**. A thick, strong pipe connects the master cylinder with slave cylinders on each side of the disc. The hydraulic pressure is transferred to the pistons in the slave cylinders. These force the brake pads on to the disc. Friction then slows the wheel down.

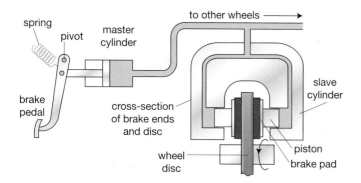

A braking system.

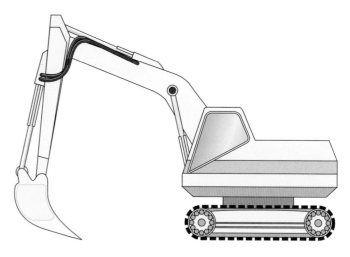

This excavator uses hydraulic pressure to produce the huge forces needed to dig into the ground and then to lift earth out of the hole.

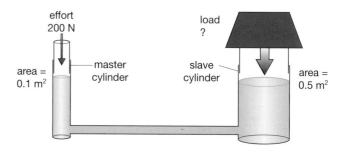

A hydraulic jack.

Questions

1   Why do the pipes containing the fluid in the excavator's hydraulic system need to have thick walls?

2   It can be very dangerous if a bubble of air gets into the hydraulic braking system of a car. Suggest why.

3   Why do scientists think of hydraulic jacks as '*force multipliers*'?

Questions

1 The table below shows how a spring stretches when it has a load suspended from it.

Load in N	0	1	2	3	4	5	6	7
Extension in mm	0	12	24	36	48	60	78	99

a) Sketch a graph of the spring's extension (y-axis) against the load (x-axis).
b) What would the extension be for a load of:
i) 3.5 N ii) 5.5 N iii) 8.0 N?
c) Why can't you use your graph to predict what would happen with a load of 20 N?

2 An athlete uses a 'chest expander' to build up his muscles.

When he has two springs on the chest expander, he needs a force of 200 N to stretch them fully apart.
a) What force would he need if he took one of the springs off?
b) What force would he need if he added another identical spring so that there were three to stretch?

3 An exploration robot weighs 2000 N on Earth where the strength of gravity is 10 N/kg.
a) What is the **mass** of the robot on Earth?
b) What is the **mass** of the robot on Mars?
c) What is the **weight** of the robot on Mars where the strength of gravity is 3.7 N/kg?

4 The diagram shows two weights on a plank resting on a pivot.

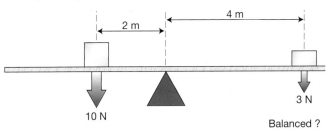

a) Prove that the plank is not balanced.
b) Describe exactly how you could balance it by adding a weight to one side.

5 The diagram shows an Inuit fisherman walking across soft snow.

Explain why he is wearing snow-shoes. Use the following words in your answer:

force   weight   pressure   area   sink

6 How could you use an old, plastic lemonade bottle to prove that water pressure increases with depth below the surface? Draw a diagram to show what you think would happen.

7 The table below shows how a rubber band stretches when it has a load suspended from it.

Load in N	0	1	2	3	4	5	6
Length in mm	52	67	82	97	110	120	125
Extension in mm	0	15					

a) Copy the table and fill in the missing values.
b) Sketch a graph of the rubber band's extension (y-axis) against the load (x-axis).
c) What, approximately, is the Hooke's law limit for the rubber band?

15

Why study movement?
What are speed and acceleration?
How do we make things move?
How do we make things stop?

Wherever we look in the universe we find things that are moving. Animals, including humans, are clearly able to move and we can build 'machines' such as cars, boats and aeroplanes for transport. However, we also find motion in less obvious places.

On a very small scale, the tiny particles which make up atoms are always on the move.

At the other end of the size scale, huge galaxies are made up of millions of stars moving around. Even our own planet orbits the Sun in a regular pattern.

By studying moving things, scientists can find laws or patterns which 'fit' the movement or motion. This means that they can predict how other things will move.

Car designers use these laws to improve the performance of new models. Aerospace engineers use them to calculate how to put rockets into space and satellites into orbit. Astronomers can find out more about the universe by observing and measuring how stars move. Athletes can even improve their performances by studying the science of motion.

There is no end to the use which we can make of the laws of motion.

Speed

What do we mean by speed?

Speed tells us how fast a thing is moving. For example, the speed of a car tells us how fast it is moving by telling us how far it will move in a set time. Look at the car speedometers drawn below. Car 1 is travelling at a speed of 100 km per hour (100 km/h). If it stays at this speed it will travel a distance of 100 km in one hour.

Car speedometers

Car 2 is travelling more slowly at 80 km/h. At this speed the car travels just 80 km in one hour.

From the speed and the time it is easy to work out how far the car will travel. Table 1 opposite gives some examples for cars 1 and 2.

What do you notice about the numbers?

We can say that;

$$\textbf{distance} = \textbf{speed} \times \textbf{time}$$

We can use symbols;

$$s = vt$$
(s = distance, v = speed, t = time.)

The speed is also useful because we can use it to work out how long a journey will take.

Table 2 opposite gives some examples for cars 1 and 2. What do you notice about the numbers?

Questions

1 A sports car travels at its top speed of 200 km/h. How far will it travel in **a)** 5 hours **b)** 30 minutes?

2 A train travels at 180 km/h. How far will it travel in 4 hours?

3 A snail travels at 50 cm/h. How far will it travel in **a)** 3 hours **b)** 1.5 hours?

4 A sports car travels at its top speed of 200 km/h. How long will it take to travel
a) 400 km **b)** 50 km?

5 Concorde travels at 2300 km/h. How long will it take to travel from London to New York (6900 km)?

6 A snail travels at 50 cm/h. How long will it take to cross a flower bed which is 125 cm wide?

Table 1

car	speed	time	distance travelled
1	100 km/h	½ h	50 km
1	100 km/h	1 h	100 km
1	100 km/h	2 h	200 km
2	80 km/h	½ h	40 km
2	80 km/h	1 h	80 km
2	80 km/h	2 h	160 km

Table 2

car	length of journey (distance)	speed (average)	time taken
1	200 km	100 km/h	2 h
1	350 km	100 km/h	3½ h
2	40 km	80 km/h	½ h
2	200 km	80 km/h	2½ h

We can say that;

$$\textbf{time taken} = \frac{\textbf{distance travelled}}{\textbf{speed}} \quad \text{or, in symbols, } t = \frac{s}{v}$$

Miles per hour (mph) and kilometres per hour (km/h) are very useful units for measuring the speed of things like cars and trains. For other things it is often useful to measure the speed in metres per second (m/s).

We can still use the same 'laws';

$$\text{distance} = \text{speed} \times \text{time} \qquad \text{time} = \frac{\text{distance}}{\text{speed}}$$

7 A bullet from a gun travels at 600 m/s.

How far does the bullet travel in 2 s?

How long would it take to travel
a) 300 m **b)** 150 m?

8 A sprinter can run at an average speed of 10 m/s. How long does he take to run **a)** 100 m **b)** 60 m? Why do you think that the athlete cannot run 800 m in 80 s?

9 In air, sound travels at around 300 m/s. How long does it take to travel 1500 m?

10 A goal keeper shouts at a footballer 100 m away. How long does it take the goal keeper's message to arrive?

Measuring speed

We have seen that if we divide the distance travelled by something which is moving by the time taken to cover that distance, we get the speed. When measuring speed we can use this formula;

$$\frac{\text{distance}}{\text{time}} = \text{speed}$$

Activities

Measuring the speed of cars

For things like cars we can measure how much time they take to travel a fairly large distance.

Choose a road where cars travel at almost steady speeds. Why would near a corner or close to a set of traffic lights not be good places?

Measure the distance between two lamp posts or other fixed objects. These markers should be about 50 m apart.

A person with a stop watch should stand at the first marker. Another person stands at the second marker.

As a car passes the person doing the timing starts the stop watch. As the car passes the second person he or she must signal for the watch to be stopped. It will take practice before you can time accurately.

Some sample results are given below. A calculator helps!

SAFETY

1   Keep well clear of the road. You should not stand on the kerb.

2   Take care not to distract drivers with your signals.

Car	Distance between markers (in m)	Time Taken (in s)	Speed (in m/s)
1	65	5.0	65/5.0 = 13.0
2	65	4.6	65/4.6 = 14.1
3	65	3.2	65/3.2 = 20.3

Sample results

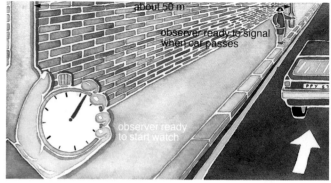

Investigating car speeds

Using your results

After measuring the speed of about fifty cars you should be able to answer these questions;

a) What was the fastest that anyone drove during your investigation?

b) What was the 'average' speed of the cars in your survey?

c) What fraction of the cars were breaking the speed limit? The conversion chart below may help.

speeds		
mph	**km/h**	**m/s**
30	48	13
40	64	18
50	80	22
60	97	27
70	113	31
80	129	36
90	145	40
100	161	45
All to the nearest whole number.		

Questions

1   In an Olympic swimming competition, an electric clock starts when the starter's gun is fired. The clock is stopped when the swimmer touches the end of the pool.

Work out the average speed for each of these swimmers.

a) Backstroke . . . 100 m in 60 s

b) Breaststroke . . . 200 m in 140 s

c) Butterfly . . . 200 m in 120 s

d) Freestyle . . . 400 m in 230 s

Speed-time graphs

When we make 'real' journeys our speed changes many times. Think of a train journey. When you get on the train it is not moving. As it leaves the station it gains speed or accelerates. On a long straight track the train can keep to a constant speed. The driver will need to change the speed as the train approaches bends, level crossings and stations. We can show all these variations on a speed–time graph.

The graph below shows the speed of a car during part of a journey through a town. We can tell several things from the graph.

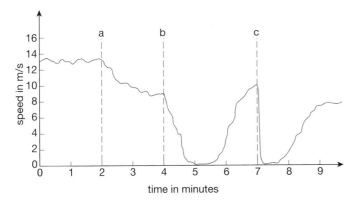

Speed-time graph for a car journey

a) For the first two minutes the driver was driving at an average speed of 13 m/s. During the next two minutes the speed was lower. Perhaps there was more traffic.
b) At a time of four minutes, the driver slowed down and then stopped. The car did not move for almost a minute. Perhaps the driver had to stop at a pedestrian crossing.
c) At a time of seven minutes, the car stopped very suddenly. Perhaps a child ran out into the road and the driver had to do an emergency stop.
d) After about 30 seconds, the car moved off again. Obviously there was no accident after the emergency stop.

One of the things we can work out from a speed–time graph is the distance which the moving object has travelled.

The area under a speed–time graph is equal to the distance travelled.
This rule works for any shape of speed-time graph. The example is for an aircraft stopping after landing.

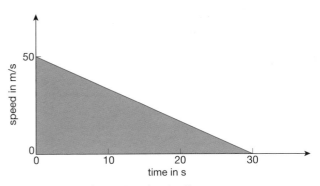

Speed-time graph for an aircraft on landing

The area of any triangle is given by half its base length multiplied by its height. For this triangle the area is:

$$(\tfrac{1}{2} \times 30\,\text{s}) \times 50\,\text{m/s} = 15\,\text{s} \times 50\,\text{m/s} = \textbf{750\,m}.$$

The runway must be at least 750 m long for this aircraft to land safely.

Questions

1 The speed–time graph below shows (roughly) the speed of a sprinter in a 100 m race.

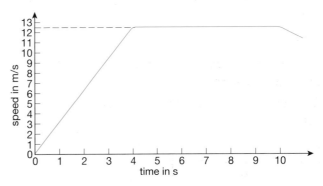

Speed-time graph for a sprinter

a) How long did it take for the sprinter to reach top speed?
b) What was his top speed?
c) What was the sprinter's speed after 2 s?
d) What was the sprinter's speed after 1 s?
e) How far had the sprinter run after 4 s? (*Hint:* the area under the graph is a triangle).
f) How far had he run after 10 s?

Changing speed and direction

The modern study of motion owes much to Sir Isaac Newton. He was an English mathematician and scientist who, amongst other things, worked to find laws which would explain the movements of planets and things on Earth. He is remembered now for the 'laws of motion' which he set out.

Newton's first law says: 'objects will continue to travel in the same direction with the same speed unless an unbalanced force acts on them.'

What do we mean by unbalanced forces?

Forces can be thought of as 'pushes' or 'pulls'. The size of a force is measured in units called **newtons**.

When an object is pulled by two forces of equal size but **in opposite directions**, the forces will balance each other out.

Newton realized that a thing will only change its speed or direction of travel when pulled by a force which is not balanced by other forces.

This is a very important idea. In everyday life we often think that a force is needed just to keep something moving at the same speed. In fact this force is needed to overcome friction. Friction is a force which acts against motion.

The best way to understand Newton's first law is to think of a spaceship moving in outer space so far from any star or planet that there is no gravity.

The spaceship has no engine to push it but there is no friction or other force to slow it down. It just travels on and on at the same speed and in the same direction.

The spaceship could be speeded up or slowed down by firing little rockets fixed to it. These would give a force to change the spaceship's speed or direction.

Things which are not moving have a speed of 0 m/s. These stationary objects obey Newton's first law too. Quite simply, as long as there are no unbalanced forces acting on the object, it will not start to move.

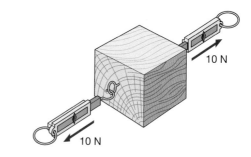

These forces balance. The block does not move.

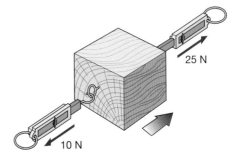

These forces do not balance. The block moves as if it was being pulled by a force of 15 N to the right.

Space capsule; obeying Newton's laws

Activities

Try to find out about Sir Isaac Newton.
  a) When was he born? When did he die?
  b) Where was he at university?
  c) What was the name of the book which contained his laws of motion? When was it published?
  d) What other scientific work did he do?
  e) What did he have to do with
  i) the Houses of Parliament
  ii) the Royal Mint?

Acceleration

When an unbalanced force acts on a moving object in the direction of its travel, the object's speed changes. The force may make it speed up but if it is in the opposite direction it will slow the object down.

Acceleration tells us how fast the speed of something is changing.

Starting from rest, each of the cars (shown opposite) can get up to a speed of 60 + miles per hour (30 m/s). Car A takes 10 s to reach 60 + mph. Car B can reach 60 + mph in just 6 s! Car B has the greater acceleration.

Acceleration can be shown very clearly on a speed–time graph. The one shown opposite has two lines; one for car A and one for car B.

The line for the sports car (B) is steeper than the line for car A. **A steep slope on a speed–time graph means a large acceleration.**

We calculate the acceleration by working out how much the speed changes in one second. For example, a racing car starts from rest. After 6 s it has accelerated to a speed of 30 m/s. Its speed has changed by 30 m/s in 6 s. In one second its speed would have changed by 30/6 = 5 (m/s)/s.

We can say the units as 'metres per second, per second'. This is because the acceleration tells us how much the speed has changed (in metres per second) in each second. [The units are often written as m/s².]

$$\text{acceleration} = \frac{\text{change in speed}}{\text{time taken}}$$

Worked example

1 A sprinter starts from rest (0 m/s) and takes four seconds to get up to a speed of 12 m/s. What is the acceleration?

The change of speed is 12 m/s − 0 m/s = 12 m/s. The time taken is 4 s.

$$\text{acceleration} = \frac{12 \text{ m/s}}{4 \text{ s}} = \mathbf{3\,m/s^2}$$

Ready, steady, go!

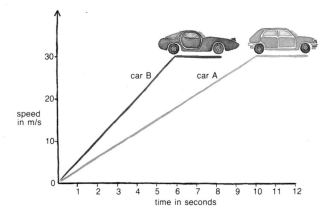

Questions

1 The table shows how the speed of a car changes with time.

After	0 s	1 s	2 s	3 s	4 s
Speed	0 m/s	2 m/s	4 m/s	6 m/s	8 m/s

a) What is the acceleration of the car?
b) If it continues to accelerate steadily, how fast will it be going after i) 8 s ii) 10 s iii) 13 s?
c) Would it be sensible to predict how fast the car would be going after 100 s? Why?

2 A plane waits on the runway before take-off. It then accelerates at an average acceleration of 3 m/s² for 27 s before it lifts off.
What is the plane's take-off speed?

3 How would you explain to one of your friends why the unit for speed is m/s but the unit for acceleration is m/s²?

Slowing things down

Friction

Our everyday experiences of motion do not seem to fit Newton's first law. We know that if we stop pedalling our bicycle it will slow down and stop. It is as if we need to keep pushing with a force just to keep a steady speed! However, this force is needed to balance other forces which act against motion. One of these is called **friction**.

Friction always appears when we try to slide one thing over another. This is because all surfaces, even polished ones, are rough when seen under a microscope. If we try to push one surface over another, the rough pieces catch on each other. This causes a force against our push.

When we want things to keep moving, friction is a nuisance because we have to use energy to overcome it. **Lubricants** such as oil can make things move more easily. When we want things to stop we can use friction. When bicycle brake blocks rub on the rim of the wheel, the friction slows the bicycle down.

Surface of a piece of paper greatly magnified

Sliding surfaces

Air resistance

When cars, bicycles and other things try to move in air, there is a force against them called **air resistance**. This is because air is made up of gases. The molecules in these gases bump into moving objects causing a force against the motion. At low speeds this is only a small force. At higher speeds it becomes much larger. Air resistance can be reduced by using shapes which let the air 'slip' past more easily. This is called **streamlining**.

Now that we have met friction and air resistance we can see how Newton's first law applies.

Bicycle brakes; using friction

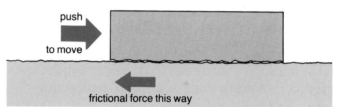

Accelerating　　　　*Steady speed*　　　　*Decelerating*

To accelerate, the force from the engine must be bigger than the forces of friction and air resistance put together.

At steady speed, the forward force will just balance the forces of friction and air resistance.

To stop a car the driver takes his foot off the accelerator pedal. This reduces the force from the engine. He also puts on the brakes. This makes the friction much larger.

Stopping a car

A car driver needs to be able to stop in a short distance to avoid accidents. To stop the car, the driver presses on the brake pedal. This makes the brake pads or brake 'shoes' rub against the wheels. The friction makes the car slow down but it takes some time before the car stops completely.

To find the stopping distances of a car a simple test can be carried out. The driver drives the car at a steady speed. At a given signal, the brakes are applied to bring the car to rest as quickly as possible without losing control. This is sometimes called an emergency stop.

The speed-time graph opposite shows what happened in a test where the car was moving at 12 m/s (about 30 mph).

The first thing to notice is that the car did not start slowing down until 0.75 s after the signal. This is how long it took the driver to react. It is sometimes called '**thinking time**'. While the driver was thinking, the car travelled 9 m!

Even with good brakes the car takes about 2.5 s to stop. During this time it travels 15 m more.

You can see that even at a fairly low speed of about 30 mph, a car takes about 24 m to stop. If the car moves at higher speeds it will take a much longer distance to stop. At 30 m/s (about 70 mph) the total stopping distance is 112.5 m: longer than a football pitch!

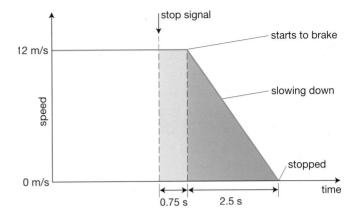

Thinking time = 0.75 s
Distance travelled during thinking time = 12 m/s × 0.75 s = 9 m
Distance travelled during braking = ½ × 2.5 × 12 = 15 m
Total stopping distance = 9 m + 15 m = 24 m

Questions

1 Alcohol in the bloodstream slows down a person's reactions. Why is a driver who has been drinking alcohol more likely to have an accident?

2 A driver is travelling at 24 m/s (about 55 mph) on a motorway in fog when he sees that there has been an accident 50 m in front. He takes 0.5 s to react before pressing on the brake pedal. The brakes take 4 s to stop the car.
   a) Draw a speed-time graph to show what happens. Your time axis needs to go from 0 to 5 s.
   b) Work out the total stopping distance.
   c) Comment on your answer.

Factors affecting stopping distance

The distance taken to stop a car depends on the speed of the car and the driver's reaction time. It also depends on the road surface and the condition of the car's brakes and tyres.

If the tyre tread pattern is worn, or if the road is wet or icy, there is less friction between the tyres and the road. It therefore takes much longer to stop the car.

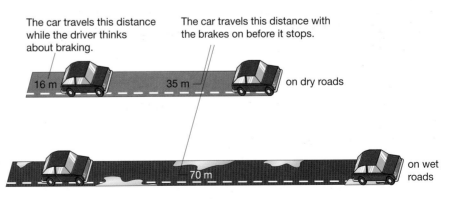

The car travels this distance while the driver thinks about braking.

The car travels this distance with the brakes on before it stops.

16 m   35 m   on dry roads

70 m   on wet roads

Stopping distances.

Gravity, falling and air resistance

If you hang a block of iron from a piece of string, the downward force (**weight**) is balanced by an upward force in the string (**tension**). The iron block stays at rest. If you cut the string, the weight makes the block accelerate downwards. On Earth, gravity makes falling objects **accelerate** at about 10 m/s². This means that after 1 s the block will be falling at 10 m/s; after 2 s it is falling at 20 m/s; after 3 s it is falling at 30 m/s and so on.

This is only true for objects falling in a vacuum. In air, a frictional force called **air resistance** acts against gravity and so reduces the acceleration. The faster the motion, the greater the air resistance.

We use this when we use a parachute. When air resistance balances the weight of the falling person, there is no acceleration. The person falls at a steady speed or **terminal velocity**.

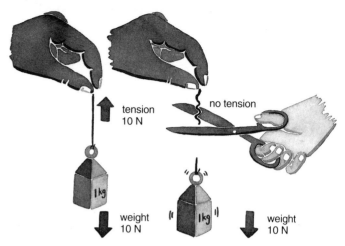

Balanced forces - no acceleration.   *Unbalanced forces - mass accelerates.*

Skydiver just after leaving the plane.

Weight accelerates the skydiver.

Skydiver without parachute open, falling at terminal velocity.

Skydiver's weight is balanced by air resistance.

Skydiver with parachute open, falling at terminal velocity.

Skydiver's weight is balanced at a low speed by the parachute's air resistance.

Questions

1 Skydivers like to fall for as long as possible before they open their parachutes. Suggest why they spread their bodies out flat as they jump out of the plane.

2 Beginners at parachuting are given large parachutes. Explain why this helps to reduce injuries.

3 Parachutists carry a spare parachute for emergencies. This is much smaller than the main parachute. Explain why you are much more likely to break a leg if you have to use your emergency parachute. (There are two reasons – think carefully.)

Activities

1 Investigate how the time taken to fall from a fixed height varies with the size of the parachute.

2 Investigate whether the time taken to fall from a fixed height depends on the weight the parachute carries.

3 Design an experiment to measure the terminal velocity of a parachute.

1 Sue works in an office in the town centre. She lives 3 km away. In the mornings she can walk to work in 30 minutes. If she cycles it only takes 20 minutes.

a) What is her average speed when walking?

b) What is her average speed on a bike?

c) If Sue drives her car to work her average speed is 4 km/h. How long does the car journey take?

2 The car below is a drag racer. It is designed to race at high speeds over short distances.

To stop, it uses ordinary brakes and a parachute. How does the parachute help the car to stop quickly?

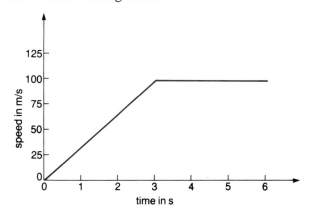

Drag racer

3 The graph below shows how the speed of a drag racer varies during a race.

Speed-time graph for a dragster.

a) How fast was the drag racer going after:
i) 1 s ii) 2 s iii) 5 s?

b) What was the acceleration of the drag racer in the first three seconds?

c) Roughly how long did the drag racer take to reach 60 mph (27 m/s)?

d) How far had the drag racer travelled in 6 s?

4 Oil is a lubricant. This means that it can reduce the friction between moving parts.

a) Why is it good to oil the axle of a bicycle wheel?

b) Why would it be dangerous to put oil on the rim of a bicycle wheel?

5 The downhill skier shown has wax on the bottom of his skis. Suggest why this helps him to travel faster down the course.

Downhill skier

What things can you see in the photograph which help to reduce air resistance? (*Hint*: there are at least three things.)

6 The poster shown below was designed to persuade people not to drink and drive.

a) Explain why it is dangerous to drive after drinking alcohol.

b) Why is this even more dangerous on a wet night?

Do posters like this work?

What are 'physical states'?
How can we explain their behaviour?
How does heating affect materials?

The substances around us can exist in three forms: solid, liquid, and gas. We call these the three **physical states**. The photographs on this page show typical solids and liquids, and containers full of gas.

Most materials can exist in all three physical states. Perhaps the best example is water. It comes out of the freezer as a solid (ice), out of the tap as a liquid, and out of a boiling kettle as a gas (steam). Heating or cooling water may change its state.

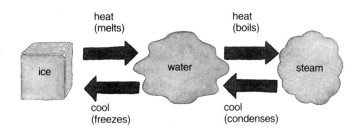

Liquids do not have well-defined shapes and they flow. When a liquid is poured into a jar or bottle it takes up the shape of the container, but only up to a certain level. The liquid has a well-defined volume which can be measured using a measuring cylinder.

Liquids take the shape of whatever container they are in but have a fixed volume.

Solids have well-defined, rigid shapes. The crystalline solids shown have flat faces and sharp edges. Like all solids they keep their shape and do not flow over surfaces.

Gases do not have a well-defined shape. When a gas is placed in a container it quickly takes up any available space. Gases can also flow and it is possible to pour heavy gases from one container to another.

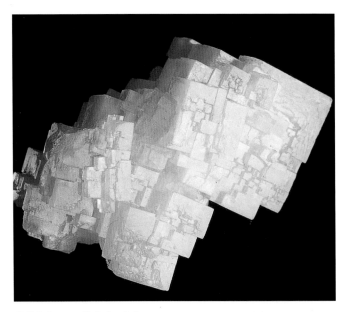

Solids have well-defined shapes.

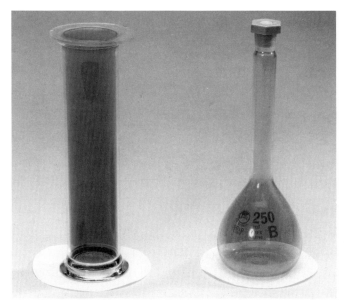

Gases take up all the available space.

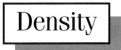

Is it right to say that lead is heavier than aluminium? Not always – it depends on the sizes of the pieces of lead and aluminium. To make a fair comparison, we have to make sure that their **volumes** are the same. The diagram shows the masses when we compare blocks which have a volume of 1000 cm³.

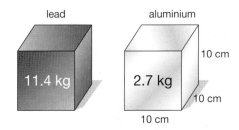

Lead is denser than aluminium.

The lead has a greater **density** than aluminium. It has a greater mass packed into the same volume.

This is how we calculate density:

$$\textbf{density} = \frac{\textbf{mass}}{\textbf{volume}}$$

Example

A lorry holds 5 m³ of ready-mixed concrete. The mass of the concrete is 4000 kg. What is the density of the concrete?

volume of concrete = 5 m³

mass of concrete = 4000 kg

density of concrete = $\dfrac{4000 \text{ kg/m}^3}{5}$ = **800 kg/m³**

1 m³ is a very big volume so it is often better to calculate densities in units of **g/cm³**. This is the mass, in grams, of a block 1 cm × 1 cm × 1 cm. The table opposite gives some common densities.

material	density (g/cm³)
gold	19.3
mercury	13.6
lead	11.4
iron	7.9
aluminium	2.7
water (at 4°C)	1.0
wood (varies)	0.7
cork	0.3

Table of densities.

Density of a rectangular, solid block

We can find the volume of a rectangular block by measuring the sides and using this formula:

volume = length × breadth × height

We can find the mass of a block by putting it on a balance.

Example

mass of gold block = <u>772 g</u>

volume of gold block = 1 cm × 5 cm × 8 cm = <u>40 cm³</u>

$\dfrac{\text{density}}{\text{of gold}}$ = $\dfrac{\text{mass}}{\text{volume}}$ = $\dfrac{772 \text{ g}}{40 \text{ cm}^3}$ = **19.3 g/cm³**

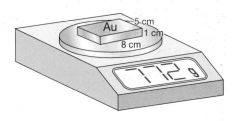

Finding the density of gold!

Questions

1 What is the mass of a rectangular iron block, 10 cm × 20 cm × 30 cm?

2 A wooden cube with 5 cm sides has a mass of 100 g. What is its density?

3 a) What do you notice about the density of water?
b) Do you notice any difference between the materials above water in the density table and those below?

Measuring density

It is easy to calculate density when we have a nice, rectangular block of solid. However, if we have an irregular solid or even a liquid or a gas, we have to use other methods. The formula is always the same. Follow the steps below to work out densities.

$$\text{density} = \frac{\text{mass}}{\text{volume}}$$

Density of an irregular solid

1 Find the mass using a balance.

2 Find the volume by submerging the solid in some water in a measuring cylinder. The rise in water level gives you the volume of the solid.

3 Calculate the density of the solid.

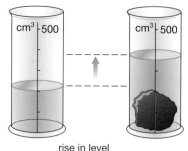

rise in level
= volume of solid

Measuring the density of an irregular solid.

Density of a liquid

1 Find the mass of a measuring cylinder. Add the liquid and find the total mass. Take away the mass of the empty measuring cylinder to get the mass of the liquid.

2 Read the volume of the liquid from the measuring cylinder.

3 Calculate the density of the liquid.

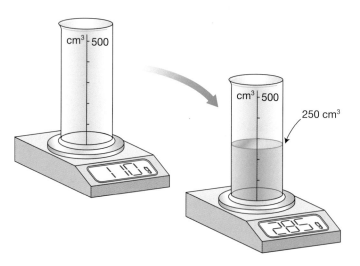

Measuring the density of a liquid.

Density of a gas

1 Remove the air from a strong, gas-tight flask using a vacuum pump. Find the mass of the empty flask using an accurate electronic balance.

2 Fill the flask with gas and then find the total mass. Take away the mass of the empty flask to find the mass of the gas.

3 Fill the flask with water. Pour the water into a measuring cylinder to find the volume of the flask.

4 Calculate the density of the gas.

Measuring the density of a gas

mass of empty flask (vacuum) = 123.1 g

mass of flask + air = 123.7 g

mass of air = 123.7 − 123.1 = 0.6 g

volume of water to fill flask = 520 cm³

density of air $\dfrac{0.6\,\text{g}}{520\,\text{cm}^3}$ = 0.001 g/cm³

Question

1 Estimate (i) the mass of water in a swimming pool and (ii) the total mass of air in all the rooms of your home. Show your working for both.

The kinetic theory of matter

The kinetic theory explains the behaviour of solids, liquids, and gases in terms of moving particles. When these particles are close together they attract each other. This gives us the following models:

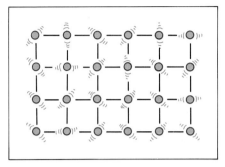

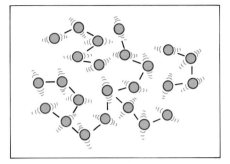

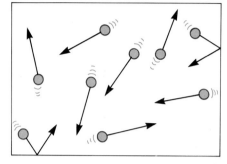

*In a **solid**, strong forces of attraction hold the atoms or molecules together in a regular grid or lattice. The particles vibrate but cannot break free. The solid has a fixed shape and volume.*

*In a **liquid**, the molecules are close together but they have enough energy to move about. As a result liquids can flow. At the surface the molecules attract one another forming a kind of skin above the liquid.*

*In a **gas**, the molecules are far apart and are moving so quickly that they do not really attract each other. They move in straight lines but have many collisions with other molecules and with the walls of the container they are in.*

We cannot see individual molecules in a solid, liquid, or gas. However, there is a lot of indirect evidence which makes us believe that they are constantly in motion.

Diffusion

When the cap is taken off a bottle of strong perfume the smell gradually spreads out. After a few minutes it can be detected several metres away. We say that the perfume's vapour (gas) has **diffused**. This means that some of the molecules which were in the bottle have escaped and moved across the room. On the way, they have collided with the moving molecules in the air, so their progress has been rather slow.

Diffusion can also take place in liquids, as demonstrated by Activity 1 opposite.

Brownian motion

We can get a better idea of molecular motion by looking at small particles of smoke suspended in air. A small glass cell is filled with smoke from a burning waxed straw. Through a microscope hundreds of bright specks can be seen. These are due to light reflecting from relatively large pieces of carbon and oil in the smoke.

If you look carefully you will see that these specks are moving in a jerky, zig-zagging motion. This is because the smoke particles are being bombarded by fast-moving molecules in the air. This random motion is

called **Brownian motion**. It is named after a Scottish scientist, Robert Brown. In 1827 Brown noticed that pollen grains moved jerkily when placed in water. In this case, the tiny pollen grains are being bombarded by fast-moving water molecules.

Surface tension

Evidence that molecules attract each other can be found from looking at the surfaces of liquids. These behave as if they were covered with a thin elastic skin. This is because the molecules in the surface layer are attracted to the molecules in the liquid below them.

Activities

1   Take a glass Petri dish or a white saucer and fill it with water. Then carefully place one drop of ink from a pipette in the centre of the water. Do not stir the water. Watch as the ink particles gradually diffuse outwards.
Design an experiment to calculate the average speed of diffusion for ink into water.

2   Fill a glass with water. Carefully add more water until the surface is above the rim. Sketch the top of the glass and the surface of the water. How does your diagram show that water molecules attract each other?

3   Put a very thin layer of lard or butter on a small plate. Put two or three drops of water on the plate. Sketch the shape of each drop as seen from the top and the side. How does this show that water molecules attract each other?

Using the kinetic theory

The kinetic theory gives us models for solids, liquids, and gases. These models can be used to explain some things which you may have noticed happening.

Expanding solids

Solids **expand** when they are heated. They don't usually expand much, but expanding solids can cause problems for engineers. For example, a 1 m length of steel expands 0.01 mm when its temperature rises by 1 °C. So a 100 m bridge would be 4 cm longer in summer (+30 °C) than in winter (−10 °C)! Engineers leave gaps at the ends of bridges to allow for this expansion. Without these gaps, the forces generated by the expanding metal could damage the bridge.

In steel the atoms are held in a regular structure called a **lattice**. Within the lattice the atoms vibrate. When the steel is heated the particles gain more energy and so vibrate more vigorously. This means that, on average, the atoms are further apart. The solid expands in all directions but keeps the same shape.

On cooling the atoms vibrate less as they lose energy and so the metal **contracts**.

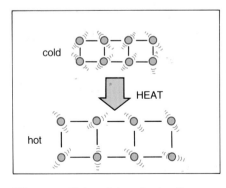

When a metal is heated the molecules vibrate more. On average they are further apart – the metal has expanded.

Conducting solids

The atoms in a metal are held in place by the forces between them. These bonds link the atoms together. When one end of a metal rod is heated the atoms near that end start to vibrate more vigorously. This makes nearby atoms vibrate more, and so gradually energy is passed along the rod. This is called **conduction**.

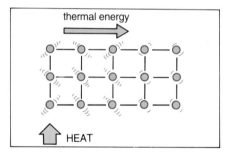

The molecules vibrate more vigorously when heated. Some of this energy is passed to neighbouring molecules, which pass it to their neighbours, and so on.

Evaporating liquids

In a liquid the molecules vibrate and move around, but they are still close enough to attract each other. The molecules stay under the surface layer. However, not all the molecules move at the same speed. Some move more quickly than average and some move more slowly. Sometimes a molecule gains enough energy to break free of the surface and escape. This is **evaporation**.

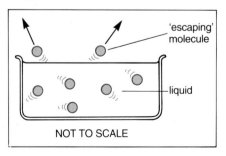

Only high-energy molecules can escape from the liquid.

Notice that only the faster molecules can break free. As a result the average speed of the molecules left is lower. This means that the liquid has a slightly lower temperature. Evaporation of a liquid causes cooling.

Questions

1 Explain, using the kinetic theory, why the handle of a metal spoon gets hot when the other end is dipped into hot tea.

2 A motorist travelling on a motorway notices that it is made up of concrete slabs 25 m long separated by a thin strip of bitumen (tar). An engineer says that these are **expansion joints**. Suggest why the road is made in this way.

3 A nurse preparing a patient for an injection cleans the skin by rubbing it with alcohol. The patient notices that this makes the skin feel cold. Suggest why.

4 The air in a room with central heating can get very dry and this can cause furniture to crack. To prevent this an open container filled with water can be placed near a radiator. Use the kinetic theory to explain why this increases the amount of water vapour in the air. Also explain why the container has to be topped up every so often.

Molecular motion and temperature

A temperature scale gives us a simple way of comparing how hot objects are. The most commonly used temperature scale is the Celsius scale. The table below gives some common examples of temperatures on this scale. Notice that 0 °C is the temperature of melting ice and 100 °C is the temperature of boiling water.

object	temperature
surface of Sun	6000 °C
light bulb filament	2500 °C
Bunsen flame	1000 °C
boiling water	100 °C
human body	37 °C
summer day (UK)	25 °C
melting ice	0 °C
cold winter day (UK)	−10 °C
domestic deep freeze	−15 °C

What is temperature?

We have already seen that, according to the kinetic theory, molecules move more quickly when a substance is heated. The energy from the heat source is transferred to the molecules as increased kinetic energy. At the same time the substance's temperature goes up.

We can think of temperature as a measure of the (average) kinetic energy of the molecules.

We can now use kinetic energy to explain what happens when a hot object is placed in contact with a cold object.

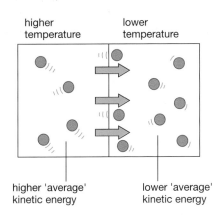

higher temperature   lower temperature

higher 'average' kinetic energy   lower 'average' kinetic energy

Thermal energy always flows from hot objects to cooler ones.

The hot object has many high-speed molecules. When these collide with the slower moving molecules in the cold object, they transfer some of their energy. The hot block gets slightly colder and the cold block gets slightly warmer. This goes on until eventually the two objects are at the same temperature. We say that they are then in **thermal equilibrium**.

When an object cools down its molecules slow down and have less kinetic energy. If we keep taking energy away the molecules will, in theory, stop moving! The temperature could never be lower because we could not take away any more energy. The lowest possible temperature is called **absolute zero**. Scientists have calculated this to be about −273 °C!

For scientific work it is convenient to use a temperature scale starting at absolute zero. The Kelvin scale starts at absolute zero and has degrees which are the same size as degrees on the Celsius scale. This makes conversions easy.

Kelvin scale	Celsius scale
1273 K	1000 °C
373 K	100 °C
273 K	0 °C
0 K	−273 °C

Questions

1 Explain the following using the kinetic theory:
   a) A spoon placed in a cup of hot tea gets hot.
   b) Adding cold milk to hot black coffee cools it down.
   c) A teapot should be heated with boiling water before tea is made in it.
   d) A kettle placed over a gas flame gets hot.

2 Convert the following temperatures to the Kelvin scale:
   a) 0 °C **b)** 100 °C **c)** 180 °C **d)** −173 °C
   e) −100 °C.

3 Convert the following temperatures to the Celsius scale:
   a) 0 K **b)** 73 K **c)** 150 K **d)** 473 K
   e) 561 K.

Changing state

When a solid is heated it may reach a temperature at which it melts and turns into a liquid. According to the kinetic theory, the molecules in the solid get more energy as they are heated. Eventually they get enough energy to break free of the forces that hold them in place in the solid. If you keep heating, the liquid will boil and turn into a gas. This is because the molecules now have enough energy to break free completely.

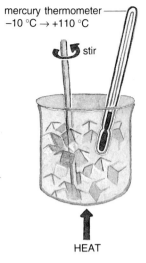

Investigating the melting and boiling of water

Activities

1   Fill a beaker almost to the top with crushed ice taken from a deep freeze. Quickly place a thermometer in the ice and record its temperature. Heat the beaker over a Bunsen burner and record the temperature of the ice/water every 30 seconds. Continue to do this until the water has been boiling for about 3 minutes. Plot the results on a graph.

The diagram below shows the general shape of the results graph. The four stages can be explained using the kinetic theory.

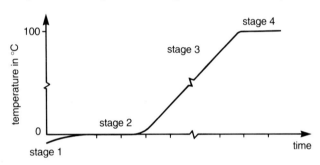

When a solid melts or a liquid boils the temperature remains constant.

Stage 1. Here the energy is raising the temperature of the ice up to 0 °C (melting point).

Stage 2. Here there is very little temperature rise. The energy is allowing molecules to break away from their fixed positions in the ice. The solid ice is turning to a liquid.

Stage 3. Here the energy is raising the temperature of the water up to 100 °C (boiling point).

Stage 4. Here there is no temperature rise. The energy is allowing molecules to break free completely. The liquid is changing to a gas.

Specific heat and specific latent heat

The energy needed to raise the temperature of 1 kg of a solid, liquid, or gas by 1 °C is called the material's **specific heat**. The energy needed to melt 1 kg of solid without changing its temperature is called the material's **specific latent heat of fusion**. The energy needed to change that 1 kg of liquid into a gas at its boiling point is called the material's **specific latent heat of vaporization**.

The diagram opposite gives the values for water. Notice that we have to supply energy to melt a solid or to boil a liquid. However, when a gas condenses or a liquid freezes energy is given out.

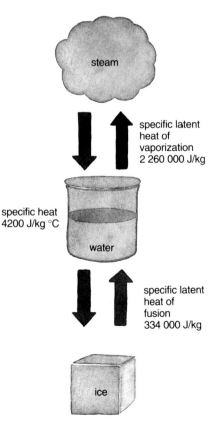

Questions

1 Copy out the passage, filling in the missing words.

Ice is a solid. When it is heated it .... and becomes water. Water is a .... which boils at 100 °C. It turns into a .... called steam. When steam cools it .... and turns back into water. At 0 °C water .... and turns into ice.

2 Diagram A shows some water in a measuring cylinder. Diagram B shows what happens when a stone is placed in the water.

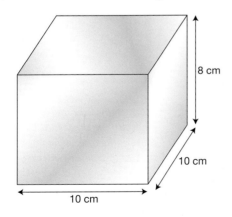

a) What is the volume of the water?
b) Estimate the reading on the measuring cylinder after the stone has been added.
c) What is the volume of the stone?

3 The diagram shows a rectangular block of aluminium. It has a mass of 2160 g.

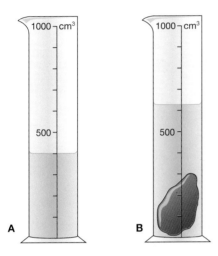

8 cm

10 cm

10 cm

a) Calculate the density of aluminium.
b) Calculate the mass of a block of gold the same size. (Density of gold = 19.3 g/cm³).

4 The diagram represents the kinetic theory model of a metal.

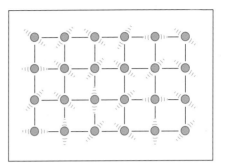

a) Is this metal a solid or a liquid? How do you know?
b) Use the model to explain how a metal conducts thermal energy (heat).

5 The kinetic theory assumes that the molecules in a material are constantly in motion.
a) What evidence do we have to support this assumption?
b) How does the kinetic theory explain the fact that liquids cool down as they evaporate?

6
a) Fill in the missing temperatures on these scales:

Celsius	Kelvin
200°	....
....	373
0°	....
....	173
−200°	....
−273°	0

b) Write a rule for changing temperatures on the Celsius scale to temperatures on the Kelvin scale.
c) Use your rule to convert the following Celsius temperatures to the Kelvin scale:
i) 300 °C ii) 150 °C iii) −50 °C.
d) Use the kinetic theory to explain why it isn't sensible to convert temperatures lower than −273 °C to the Kelvin scale.

4 Energy, work and fuels

What is 'energy'?
What is 'work'?
What are 'fuels'?
Why does burning fossil fuels cause problems?
What alternative energy sources can we use?

Plants and animals need energy for all their life processes. For example, they need energy to grow and to move. Machines need energy to do work.

Some chemicals have energy 'locked up' in their molecules. These can be used as **fuels**. For example, we can use the energy that is released when coal burns.

This tree needs energy to grow.

*This athlete needs energy to move. She also needs energy to throw the javelin. By using a force to make the javelin move she is doing **work**.*

This train needs energy to move. A huge force is needed to move the train and all its passengers. Work is done as this force moves.

*Green plants, including trees, make their own food from water and carbon dioxide in the process called **photosynthesis**. This 'traps' energy from sunlight. The Sun is the ultimate source of all the energy we use on our planet.*

Animals, including human athletes, use food as their 'fuel'. The body releases energy from the food molecules. The energy can then be used by muscle cells. Foods which contain carbohydrates are good sources of energy.

Many trains, cars and lorries use petroleum products from oil as fuel. The fuel for electric trains is the coal, oil, or gas burnt in power stations to produce electricity.

Types of energy

There are several types of energy which can be used to do work. Living things, machines and electrical appliances convert energy from one type into other forms.

Chemical energy

Energy which is produced as a result of a chemical reaction. For example: when fuel burns in an engine, when a human uses food, when a battery produces electricity.

Electrical energy

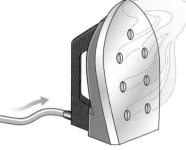

Energy due to electrical charges moving. For example: electric current in a wire.

Nuclear energy

Energy due to changes in the nuclei of atoms. For example: in the radioactive fuel in a nuclear power station.

Sound energy

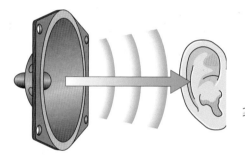

Energy carried by sound waves. For example: sound waves from a loudspeaker.

Thermal energy (heat)

Energy due to fast-moving particles in hot objects. For example: in an electric kettle, thermal energy is transferred from the heating element to the cold water.

Radiated energy

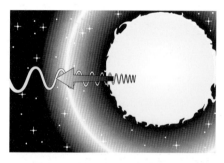

Energy carried as electromagnetic waves. For example: light from the Sun, radio waves from an aerial.

Potential energy (mechanical)

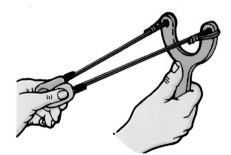

*Energy stored in materials that have been bent or stretched. For example: tightly wound springs in clocks, stretched elastic bands in a catapult. This can be thought of as **strain energy** or **spring energy**.*

Potential energy (gravitational)

Energy stored in materials that have been moved upwards so that they can now fall down. For example: a skier at the top of a mountain, a diver on a high diving board.

Kinetic energy

Energy in objects that are moving. For example: a moving car, a moving ball, a moving pendulum.

Work and energy

Work

We use chemical energy from food to do work. We do work when we use a force to make something move. For example, when we lift a weight, drag a heavy sack across the floor, or push a lawnmower, we are doing work. The amount of work depends on the size of the force and the distance we make it move.

work done = force × distance moved
        (measured in the direction of the force)

The unit of work is the **joule (J)**.

1 joule of work is done when a force of 1 newton moves 1 metre. $(1\,J = 1\,N \times 1\,m)$

Energy and work

When we do work we use energy. In fact, to do 1 J of work we need to transfer 1 J of energy. Notice that the same units are used for work and for energy.

You can find out how much energy you get from your food by looking at the nutritional information given on the packaging. The energy value is given in kilojoules (kJ). (**1 kJ = 1000 J**).

(The energy value is also given in units called kilocalories – these are the 'calories' familiar to those on diets.)

Question

1 The diagram shows an athlete lifting a weight.
    a) Where did the energy to lift the weight come from?
    b) What energy changes take place when he lifts the weight?
    c) How much work has he done?

Example

A force of 100 N is being used to push the lawnmower.

She pushes it a total of 200 m.

work done = force × distance

work done = **20000 J**

ORANGE & CAROB

6 INDIVIDUALLY WRAPPED BARS
(each bar 33.3 g)

CALORIES PER BAR – 140	
TYPICAL NUTRITIONAL CONTENT PER 100 g	
ENERGY	1758 kJ
	420 kcal
PROTEIN	8 g
AVAILABLE CARBOHYDRATE	51 g
OIL (Unsaturated Fatty Acids)	21 g
DIETARY FIBRE	13 g

Nutritional value tables include energy values.

Energy from fuels

We get a lot of the energy we need by burning fuels. The energy is released by a chemical reaction called **combustion**. The fuel reacts with oxygen to give out thermal energy (heat). A small amount of energy is needed to start the reaction, but once the fuel has been **ignited**, the reaction keeps going.

Common fuels are:

- **Wood** and **charcoal** – still used in many countries for heating homes and cooking.

- **Coal** and **coke** – used in homes and power stations.

- **Natural gas** – used in homes, factories and power stations.

- **Liquified petroleum gases** (lpg) – bottled gases, e.g. butane and propane, used where there is no natural gas supply.

- **Oil products** – used in vehicles (petrol, diesel, aviation fuel), for heating homes and in power stations (fuel oil).

How do fuels release energy?

When a fuel is lit (ignited), the energy is used to break the bonds holding the atoms in the fuel molecules together. In this natural gas molecule (methane), the bonds between the carbon and hydrogen atoms will be broken.

Once free, the atoms can react with oxygen in the air to form new molecules. The products from burning methane are water (H_2O) and carbon dioxide (CO_2). **Making bonds in the new molecules releases lots of energy.**

Using fuel to heat water

Burning fuel can be used to heat water. As thermal energy is transferred, the temperature of the water rises. **It takes 4200 J of energy to heat 1 kg of water up by 1 °C.**

Example

A gas burner is used to heat 1 kg of water which, when it was taken from the tap, was at 15 °C. The burner is turned off when the water reaches 95 °C.

Energy used = mass of water $\times$ temperature rise $\times$ 4200 J/kg/°C

Energy used = 1 kg $\times$ (95 − 15) °C $\times$ 4200 J/kg/°C

Energy used = 80 $\times$ 4200 J = **336000 J**

The combustion triangle.

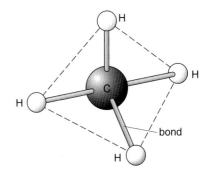

A methane molecule.

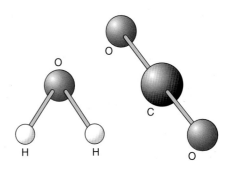

Water and carbon dioxide molecules.

Question

1   How much energy is needed:
    a) to heat 1 kg of water up by 1 °C
    b) to heat 2 kg of water up by 1 °C
    c) to heat 2 kg of water up by 10 °C
    d) to heat 0.5 kg of water up by 10 °C?

Formation of coal

Coal was formed from the remains of plants which grew in huge forests about 300 million years ago! As the plants died, they fell down and began to rot. The decaying plants formed a thick layer on the wet and swampy floor of the forest.

*The action of bacteria changed the decaying plants to **peat**. Peat is used as a fuel in some countries. It is the first stage in the formation of coal.*

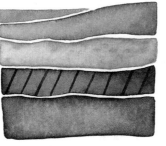

Stages in the formation of coal

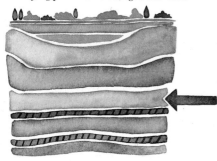

Eventually, over millions of years, the decaying plants were changed into coal.

Gradually the land sank and water covered it. Layers of mud and gravel were laid over the decaying plants. As more and more rocks were laid down by the seas above, the pressure on the peat layers increased. The temperature also got higher.

What is coal?

We can think of coal as an impure form of the element carbon. There are several different types of coal. These were formed at different pressures and temperatures under the Earth's surface.

type of coal	approximate amount of carbon	description	main mining areas in the UK
anthracite	90%	Hard, black coal. Formed at great depth.	South Wales
bituminous	60%	Formed at lower pressure than anthracite.	Nottingham Yorkshire
lignite	40%	Softer coals, sometimes brown in colour	Nottingham Yorkshire

Fossil fuels

Coal is called a **fossil fuel** because it was formed from living things. Fossils of plants can sometimes be found in lumps of coal.

Natural gas and oil are also fossil fuels. The uranium used as a fuel in nuclear power stations is not a fossil fuel. It is a naturally occurring element.

Questions

1 How do we know that ferns were alive over 300 million years ago?

2 Explain why human fossils are not found in coal.

3 How were the layers of plant material buried under mud and gravel?

4 How could you tell the difference between a piece of anthracite and a piece of lignite?

5 Why is anthracite a better fuel than lignite?

6 Suggest why the peat found in Ireland has not turned to coal.

7 Why do you think that geologists call the time when coal was being formed the **carboniferous period**?

Other fossil fuels

Hundreds of millions of years ago, while ancient forests were starting to make coal on the land, other fossil fuels were being made in the sea. We use them now as **oil** and **natural gas**.

Oil was made from the microscopic plants and animals which lived in the sea. As they died their bodies collected at the bottom of the ocean. Here they were covered by mud and sand. Over thousands of years the layers of mud and sand became very thick. This put the decaying plants and animals under pressure. High temperatures and the pressure changed them into a thick black liquid called crude oil.

The layers of sand and mud turned into rocks. We call rocks laid down by the sea, **sedimentary rocks** (see page 119). These have tiny holes in them rather like a sponge. The holes allow liquids to slowly move through the rock. The rock is **porous**.

The crude oil moved slowly through the porous rock. However, in some places the layers of rock had become folded so that the oil was trapped under solid, hard rock. The oil could not move through this **impermeable rock** and so it collected together. It is these 'pockets' of trapped oil that oil companies look for.

How do we find oil?

Large pockets of crude oil are found where layers of porous rock meet impermeable rock. We are more likely to find oil where the layers have been folded to make a 'dome' shape. Oil geologists study geological maps to find areas where the right types of rocks are found. They can then drill deep holes and remove samples of rock. This tells them what the rocks under the ground are like.

To check the shape of the rock layers, the geologists can send shock waves through the ground. They do this by setting off an explosion. They then use special microphones to record any echoes. By studying the echoes received at each microphone, the shape of the rock layers can be mapped.

All these methods are used to find areas where the oil company is **likely** to find oil or gas. The only way to find out for certain is to drill a test hole. Sometimes several bore holes will be needed before oil is found. Sometimes no oil or gas is found. Exploring for oil is very expensive!

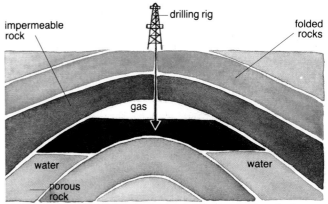

The gas and oil are trapped below a dome of impermeable rock. Once the drill gets through this rock, gas and oil will be released.

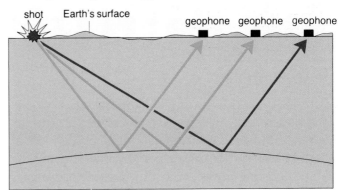

Finding oil: the sound from the explosion bounces off rock layers and the echoes are picked up by special microphones called geophones.

Questions

1 Explain why crude oil is called a 'fossil' fuel?

2 What does crude oil look like?

3 What does 'porous' mean?

4 Design an experiment to show that a stick of chalk is porous.

5 What does 'impermeable' mean?

6 What does 'geology' mean?

Fuels and other things from oil

When crude oil is pumped from the ground it is a black, smelly liquid. It is a mixture of many chemicals which, on their own, are very useful. They can be separated by a technique called **fractional distillation**. The crude oil is heated to a temperature of about 400°C. This turns it into a mixture of gases which are pumped into a tall tower. The hot gases rise up the tower.

The top is cooler than the bottom, so as the gases move upwards some of them start to turn back into liquids. Because they have different boiling points the different liquids form, and are pumped out at different heights. The diagram shows how the crude oil is separated into fractions in the fractionating tower. Notice how gases are taken off at the top, thin liquids in the middle, and thick liquids and waxes at the bottom.

Oil fractionating plant

Using the fractions

Crude oil has become one of the most important sources of **organic compounds**. Organic compounds are compounds which contain carbon atoms joined to hydrogen and sometimes other atoms. They can be very simple like methane or can contain long chains or rings of carbon atoms. These compounds are very important to industry and in our everyday lives. Crude oil supplies hundreds of organic compounds. These are used in man-made textiles like nylon and Terylene, in explosives, in paints and dyes, in cosmetics, in plastics, in car tyres, in road surfaces . . . the list is almost endless. In addition to these things, fractional distillation of crude oil gives us a number of different fuels.

Petroleum gas

Petroleum gas is a mixture of light organic compounds called alkanes. These can be turned into liquids and stored inside metal cylinders. This is useful because it gives us a portable fuel supply. Some camping stoves used bottled gas. Propane gas can be used to run gas central heating in areas where there is no supply of natural gas.

Petrol and paraffin

Petrol and paraffin are liquid fuels. Petrol is used for car engines. It contains molecules with between 5 and 10 carbon atoms. Octane is an organic compound with 8 carbon atoms. Look for this name when you are next in a garage. Paraffin is no longer a popular fuel for use in the home but some types of greenhouse heaters burn it. A special type of paraffin called kerosene can be used in the engines of jet aircraft.

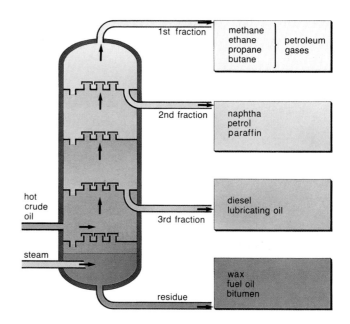

Diesel oil

Diesel oil is used for vehicles with a special type of engine. Diesel engines are very reliable but are noisier than petrol engines. Tractors, lorries, buses and ships usually have diesel engines.

Fuel oil

Fuel oil is a thick liquid which can be burnt in the boilers used to heat schools, factories and other large buildings. Some power stations use fuel oil to produce electricity.

Burning fossil fuels – a problem

All fossil fuels contain carbon. When carbon compounds burn, they release energy. This makes them good fuels. However, they also produce other things. The equation below shows what happens when natural gas (methane) burns in air.

$$CH_4\ (g)\quad +\quad 2O_2\ (g)\quad \rightarrow\quad CO_2\ (g)\quad +\quad 2H_2O\ (g)\quad +\quad \text{energy}$$

methane + oxygen → carbon dioxide + water
(gas)   (gas)   (gas)   (gas)

Natural gas is a very clean fuel. The only products are water and carbon dioxide. These escape into the air as colourless, odourless and non-toxic gases. Unfortunately, carbon dioxide is a **greenhouse gas**. This means that it helps to trap heat in the atmosphere just like the glass traps heat in a greenhouse.

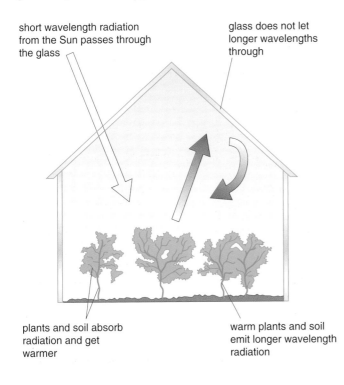

short wavelength radiation from the Sun passes through the glass

glass does not let longer wavelengths through

plants and soil absorb radiation and get warmer

warm plants and soil emit longer wavelength radiation

A real greenhouse.

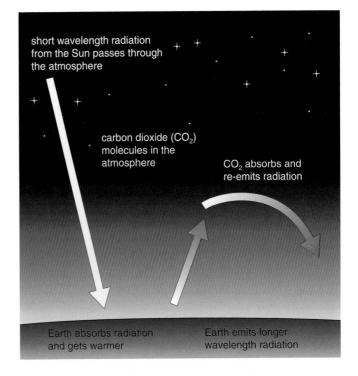

short wavelength radiation from the Sun passes through the atmosphere

carbon dioxide (CO_2) molecules in the atmosphere

CO_2 absorbs and re-emits radiation

Earth absorbs radiation and gets warmer

Earth emits longer wavelength radiation

The greenhouse effect in the atmosphere.

The greenhouse effect is good for us. Without it the Earth's average temperature would be –45 °C instead of the present +12 °C. However, in the last 150 years the amount of CO_2 in our atmosphere has risen steadily. This is mainly because we have been burning fossil fuels in our homes, factories, and cars. Scientists are worried that this will cause **global warming**. Rising temperatures would cause polar ice caps to melt, flooding places like the Netherlands and the east of England. Uneven warming of the atmosphere may also cause powerful storms.

The world's use of fossil fuels is still increasing. However, the governments of some industrialized countries have agreed to reduce CO_2 emissions in the future.

Questions

1

  a) What are *fossil fuels*?

  b) Suggest why all fossil fuels contain carbon.

2 A scientist says, "The greenhouse effect is not a bad thing, but global warming is." Do you agree? Why?

Burning fossil fuels ... more problems

Fossil fuels like coal and oil contain the element **sulphur** as an impurity. When they burn, the sulphur reacts with the oxygen in the air to make sulphur dioxide. This gas can cause serious pollution in the atmosphere.

Burning sulphur

Sulphur is a bright yellow element. When it is heated in air it starts to burn with a blue flame. The gas given off has a strong, choking smell and so this investigation is best done in a fume cabinet.

When burning sulphur is put into pure oxygen gas it burns with a bright blue flame. The gas given off is called sulphur dioxide.

sulphur + oxygen → sulphur dioxide

$$S\,(s) \quad + \quad O_2\,(g) \rightarrow \quad \quad SO_2\,(g)$$

The sulphur dioxide trapped in the gas jar can be dissolved in a little distilled water and then tested with indicators. When a piece of blue litmus paper is dipped in the solution it turns red. When Universal indicator solution is added to the solution it turns red. **These results show that sulphur dioxide gas dissolves in water to give a strong acid.**

The acid produced when sulphur dioxide is added to water is called sulphurous acid.

sulphur dioxide + water → sulphurous acid

$$SO_2\,(g) \quad + H_2O\,(l) \rightarrow \quad H_2SO_3\,(aq)$$

Sulphur dioxide pollution

Industries and power stations that burn coal, coke, or oil let sulphur dioxide escape from their chimneys. This mixes with the air and moves around as the wind blows. The sulphur dioxide dissolves in water in the air and so when it rains the rain is acidic.

Sulphur dioxide is not the only acidic gas in the atmosphere. Petrol engines give out nitrogen dioxide in their exhaust gases. This also dissolves in water to give acidic rain water. **Acid rain is a serious problem in many parts of the world.**

The effects of acid rain

The effects of acid rain on plants has a serious effect on the environment. If trees die because of acid rain then the woodland animals may also die. In fact the balance may be so upset that the environment may be changed forever.

Acid rain also causes problems in lakes. The rain makes the water in the lake slightly acidic. Some of the small organisms in the lake cannot live in acidic conditions so they die. Larger organisms, for example fish, then have less food and so some of them die. Their decaying bodies cause more pollution until the lake has very little life in it.

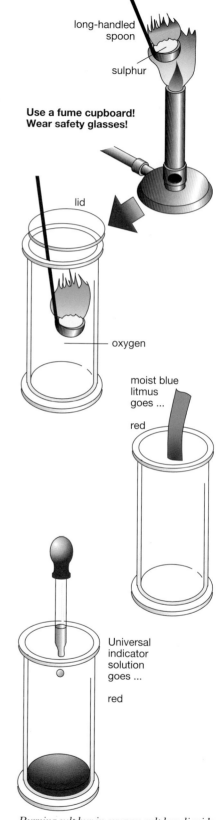

long-handled spoon

sulphur

Use a fume cupboard! Wear safety glasses!

lid

oxygen

moist blue litmus goes ...

red

Universal indicator solution goes ...

red

Burning sulphur in oxygen: sulphur dioxide gas is acidic. It has a strong, choking smell. This experiment should be done in a fume cupboard.

How long will fossil fuels last?

Over 90 per cent of all the energy used in the United Kingdom comes from fossil fuels – coal, oil, and natural gas. The supplies of these fuels are limited and we are using them up at an alarming rate.

The chart shows how long our fossil fuels will last. Of course we may find some more oil and gas but it would not make much difference to these predictions. You can see that oil and gas are likely to run out in your lifetime!

fuel	known supplies	when is it likely to run out?
natural gas	about 50 years	2050
oil	about 70 years	2070
coal	about 300 years	2300

The fact that we are running out of fossil fuels means that we must plan for the future. There are three things which we can do:

● make the best possible use of the energy we get from our fossil fuels now

● find alternative fuels to coal, oil, and gas

● find new sources of energy where we do not need to burn fuels.

Conservation

Energy conservation means making the best use of our energy supplies. It is important that we do not waste fuel in the home, in our cars, or in our industries.

When the energy we use for heating escapes, it is distributed among the many molecules of the atmosphere. It can never be recaptured or used again. This is a waste of both energy and money.

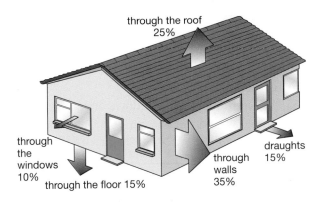

Heat loss from a house

Loft insulation

About 25 per cent (one quarter) of the energy used to heat a house escapes through the roof. This means that for every £100 spent on fuel, £25 is used to heat the air outside! This waste can be reduced by insulating the roof. This is done by covering the floor of the loft (roof space) with a layer of material which it is difficult for heat to get through. For example a thick layer of fibre-glass or mineral wool can be used. The fibres of the insulating material trap lots of air between them. Air is a poor conductor of heat and so not much energy escapes.

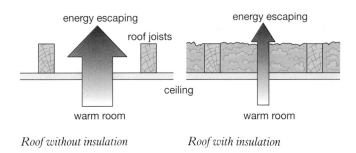

Roof without insulation   *Roof with insulation*

Loft insulation is not very difficult to install and the material is relatively cheap. The money spent on insulating the roof of a house can be saved on reduced fuel bills in about two years.

Cavity wall insulation

About one-third of the heat in our homes escapes through the walls. To prevent this modern houses are built with cavity walls. These have two layers of brick with an air space between. The air acts as a good insulator and so less heat is lost than through a solid wall.

The cavity works even better if it is filled with an insulating material. This traps the air and stops it carrying away heat by convection.

For a new house blocks of mineral fibre can be put into the cavity as the walls are being built. If the house is already built, special insulating foam can be pumped into the cavity through holes drilled in the wall. This is a job which can only be done by specialists. It is expensive so it is likely to take over five years before you save the cost in reduced fuel bills.

Windows

Most buildings have single sheets of glass in the window frames. Heat can be conducted through the glass and lost to the air outside. To prevent this a second sheet of glass can be used in the window. This is called **double glazing**.

Sometimes a second window is added to one which is already there. This is called secondary glazing. The layer of air trapped between the glass acts as a good insulator and so reduces the amount of heat lost.

It is also possible to fit double-glazed window units which have been specially made in a factory. These have two sheets of glass but the air between them is pumped out to leave a vacuum. This reduces heat loss even more.

Special double-glazing units are very expensive and may have to be fitted by experts. It can take up to thirty years to save the cost of double glazing on your fuel bills!

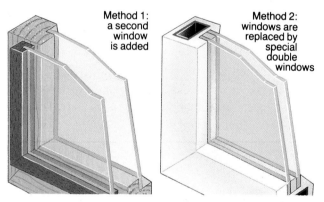

Method 1: a second window is added

Method 2: windows are replaced by special double windows

Double glazing

Other ways of cutting fuel bills

Draught excluders

Draughts let about 15 per cent of the energy escape from our homes. These can often be stopped by fixing strips of plastic or foam around the edges of doors and windows.

Strips which brush against the floor can be fixed along the bottom of doors. This lets them open and close but stops cold air from blowing in under the door. Draught excluders like these are very cheap and easy to fit. They make the house more comfortable and their cost can be recovered very quickly.

Hot water cylinder jackets

In houses, hot water is usually stored in a copper cylinder. Copper is a very good conductor of heat so the cylinder loses energy quickly. The immersion heater or boiler then has to heat the water again. Covering the cylinder with a thick 'jacket' filled with insulating material slows down the heat loss and so saves fuel. The cost of insulating the hot water tank can be recovered in a few months.

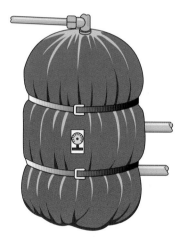

Insulating the hot water cylinder saves a lot of energy

Activities

1 Find out about energy conservation in your home.
   a) If you have a loft is it insulated? What type of insulation is it? How thick is the layer of insulation? Is the cold water tank lagged?
   b) Have you got double glazing? If you have is it secondary glazing or factory-made units? Try to find out how much it costs to have double-glazed windows fitted.
   c) Have you got cavity walls? (This may be difficult to check but you can do it by measuring the thickness of an outside wall. A solid brick wall will be about 25 cm thick. A cavity wall will be about 30 cm thick.)
   If you have got cavity walls are they filled with insulating material?
   d) Are your doors and windows draughty? Are they fitted with draught excluders? Find out how much a draught excluder costs for   i) the bottom of a door   ii) a letter box.
   e) Is your hot water tank lagged? Does the jacket fit well or are there gaps in it?

Other sources of energy

The way we use fuels in our homes has changed very much over the past hundred years or so. Originally candles and oil lamps were used for lighting. They were dirty, dangerous and did not give much light. Eventually coal gas was piped into houses. Gas lamps lit houses and streets. This was much more convenient than oil but still it did not give a good light. Finally, electricity took the place of gas and now electric light bulbs and fluorescent tubes seem to be everywhere.

Electricity has changed our lives because it can be used for lighting, heating, and to operate motors inside domestic appliances like vacuum cleaners and hair driers. Electricity is not a fuel. We produce nearly all our electricity by burning fossil fuels.

Hot water geyser

Fossil fuel to electricity

The fuel, usually oil or coal, is burnt in boilers. The energy heats water and turns it to steam. The hot steam is then piped to steam turbines. A steam turbine is like a fan. When the steam flows through it the blades of the turbine turn. This drives an electrical generator.

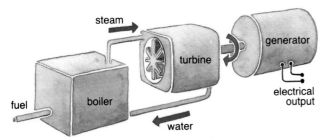

The electricity produced can be stepped up to very high voltages by a transformer and then sent all over the country using the National Grid system.

Because our supplies of coal and oil are running out and because of the pollution caused by burning fossil fuels, other ways of making electricity must be found.

Nuclear fuels

A thermal power station uses coal to heat water. This can also be done using the energy released in a nuclear reactor using uranium as a fuel.

Uranium is an alternative fuel and it has been used in the United Kingdom for many years. There is disagreement over whether we should be using nuclear fuels or not.

Geothermal energy

The inside of the Earth is very hot. No one knows exactly how this energy is generated (except that it is a radioactive process) but we do know that there are hot rocks just below the surface. Volcanoes and hot water geysers give us dramatic evidence for this.

In the future it may be possible to use the hot rocks commercially in the UK to turn water into steam which could then be used to turn turbines and generate electricity. Test drillings are already being made to find the best way of using geothermal energy.

Questions

1 **a)** Describe two advantages of gas lighting over the use of candles.
   b) Describe two advantages of electric light bulbs over gas lights.

2 Explain why electricity should not be described as a 'fuel'.

3 Explain why uranium should not be described as a 'fossil fuel'.

4 Design a method for generating electricity from the energy trapped in hot rocks below the ground. You should illustrate your answer with a clear, labelled diagram of your method.

Describe any problems which you think might occur with your method.

Renewable energy sources

Energy sources which do not use fuels dug from the Earth are called **alternative** energy sources. They use natural sources such as the sun, the tides, and the wind. Because these things will be able to supply energy for millions of years they are called renewable energy sources.

Because we have been able to get energy easily by burning coal and oil we do not have much experience of using these alternative sources of energy. There are many problems to be overcome but scientists and engineers have started to develop new ways of using renewable energy sources.

Traditional windmill

Wind power

The old windmills of England and the Netherlands show that we can use energy from the wind. These old mills were used to grind corn but when the wind did not blow the work had to stop. The fact that the wind does not blow steadily is still a problem. Windmills or, more correctly, wind turbines can be used to drive electrical generators but storing the energy is not easy. One suggestion is that we should build a large number of huge wind turbines off the coast of Scotland. The electricity could be fed into the National Grid. When the wind was blowing, other types of power stations could produce less electricity and so burn less fuel.

Modern wind turbines

Hydro-power

Around 200 years ago mills and factories were built near to fast flowing rivers. The moving water was used to turn a water wheel which then drove machinery. Old water wheels can be found throughout the counry but they are rarely used now. However, we can use flowing water to drive turbines in hydro-electric power stations.

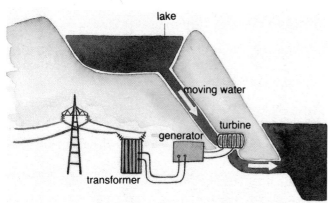

Hydro-electric power station

Hydro-electric power stations have proved very successful in some parts of the world such as

Scandinavia and North America but they are expensive to build. It is often necessary to change the surrounding countryside by building dams and diverting rivers. This may flood farmland and people may have to be moved from their homes. Some hydro-electric projects are facing problems because mud carried by the rivers is building up behind the dams and may block the turbines.

Questions

1 What is a 'renewable' source of energy? Give one example.

2 What is the main problem with trying to use wind power?

3 Why do you think that the north coast of Scotland has been suggested as a good site for wind turbines?

4 What is meant by 'hydro-power'? Write down three other words that use *hydro* to mean water.

5 What would you look for if you were trying to find a site to build a hydro-electric power station?

6 Suggest two reasons why a hydro-electric power station may not be a good idea in Ethiopia.

Solar energy

The Earth gets more than enough energy from the sun to meet all its energy needs. If we can trap and use this energy we will not need to burn fuels. Scientists and engineers are trying to find the best way to do this.

Solar panels

A panel, like this, on the roof of a house uses energy from the sun to heat water. It is called a solar panel.

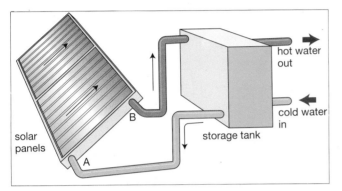

Heating water using a solar panel

Solar panels are very useful in parts of the world where the sun shines nearly every day. They are less useful in the United Kingdom because our sunshine is more variable. We also get most of our sunshine in the summer when we need less energy!

Solar cells

The calculator shown here is solar powered. The solar cells use the energy in light to produce a very small amount of electricity. This is enough to make the calculator work and so no batteries are needed. Cells like these are used to generate electricity for satellites in space.

Power from the sea

This sea is constantly in motion. Research is being carried out to see how we can use the tides and waves to produce electricity.

Tidal barrage

A tidal power station is built on a long barrier called a tidal barrage. This is a special barrier built across the mouth of a tidal river (the **estuary**).

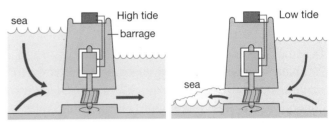

A tidal barrage. Water flows from the sea through the turbines in the barrage. Electricity is produced and the water is trapped. Water is released to flow through the turbines. These drive generators to produce electricity.

Tidal barrages are very expensive to build and, because they change the flow of the river, they can affect the environment. This may mean that sea birds and other animals can no longer live in the estuary.

Wave power

There are plans to use sea waves to generate electricity. One idea is to build huge floating generators. These would move up and down with the waves. This movement would drive the generators.

Another idea is to let the sea waves move up and down inside large tubes. As the wave moves up the air in the tube is compressed. The compressed air can then be used to turn a turbine connected to a generator.

These ideas are only experimental. Models have been made but it will be many years before full-size wave-power generators are built.

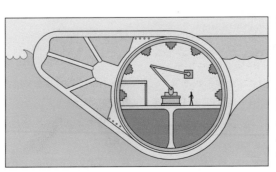
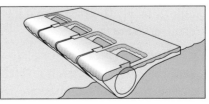

Salter's ducks are wave-powered generators. As they nod up and down on the waves (like ducks!) they generate electricity.

Energy from living things

Green plants have been trapping energy from the Sun for millions of years. They use the energy to make sugars from carbon dioxide and water. This is called **photosynthesis**. There are ways of releasing this energy, so we can think of plants as sources of renewable energy.

Fermentation

The sugars made by plants can be changed into alcohol by using yeast. The method for doing this is called **fermentation**. We use this to make alcoholic drinks like wine, but alcohol will burn and so it can be used as a fuel.

In some parts of the world, for example in Brazil and Zimbabwe, special crops like sugar cane are grown to make alcohol. It grows very quickly and the sugar it contains is very easy to ferment. The alcohol is then mixed with petrol and used by cars and lorries.

Energy from biological waste

Decaying plants can give energy. This can be easily shown by filling a vacuum flask with fresh grass clippings. A thermometer is then fixed into the neck of the flask so that its end is resting in the centre of the grass. After a few days the temperature is much higher. The energy has been released by the microbes which have started to digest the grass.

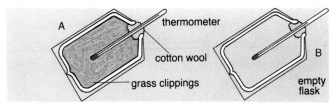

(Flask B is set up as a control. The only thing missing is grass. The control will show whether the temperature rise is due to the grass or something else.)

Using animal waste

In some parts of the world animal dung (faeces) is used as a fuel. It is dried in the sun and then burnt. Unfortunately this means that it is not being used as a fertilizer to improve the soil.

When animal and plant waste decays under the right conditions, methane gas is given off. In a modern sewage system this can be collected and used as a fuel.

Some villages in developing countries now have **biogas generators**. Animal waste is put into a tank with a lid. As microbes digest the waste, methane gas is given off. This can be used for boiling water and for cooking.

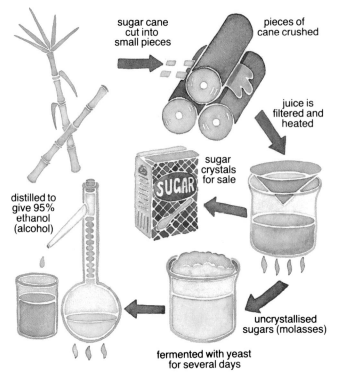

Making ethanol from sugar cane

Activities

Many gardeners build heaps of waste plant materials to make compost. The old plants rot as microbes and other organisms digest them. This produces enough heat to kill off any weed seeds on the compost heap.

Design an experiment to show that the inside of a compost heap gets hot. Your method should allow you to investigate the middle of the heap without letting in too much cold air from the outside. You may want to use plastic bottles, lengths of hosepipe, water, and thermometers.

Questions

1 Where does the energy in green plants come from?

2 Plants make sugars by photosynthesis. What gas do they use?

3 Why can we think of plants as a 'renewable' energy source?

4 Why is sugar cane a good crop to grow for making alcohol in countries like Brazil?

1 Coal is an impure form of carbon. One of the impurities is sulphur. Carbon and sulphur both burn in oxygen.

a) Write a word equation for the combustion (burning) of carbon in oxygen.

b) How could you show that the gas given off when carbon burns is carbon dioxide?

c) Write a word equation for the combustion of sulphur in oxygen.

d) How could you show that the gas given off when sulphur burns is acidic?

e) Explain why coal-fired stations in the north of England can damage trees in Norway.

2 The diagram shows a tower used for the fractional distillation of oil. The table lists some fractions and their boiling points.

Fraction	boiling point
bitumen	350 °C
lubricating oil	270 °C
diesel oil	200 °C
paraffin	150 °C
petrol	50 °C
petroleum gases	less than 20 °C

petroleum gases

6 →
5
4
3
2
1

hot, crude oil

a) Which fraction would be taken out at the bottom of the tower (level 1)?

b) What could this fraction be used for?

c) At what level could you collect petrol?

d) Which fraction is used for jet engines?

e) Name *two* things other than fuels which can be made from the chemicals extracted from crude oil.

3 a) Why is coal called a *fossil fuel*? Name one other fossil fuel.

b) Why is the uranium used in nuclear power stations **not** called a fossil fuel?

c) What is a *renewable energy source*? Give two examples.

d) Geothermal energy refers to the energy held in hot rocks.
Find three other words starting 'Geo...'
Find three words starting 'Therm...'
What do you notice?

4 The White family live in the house shown below. They spend £600 each year to heat the house. The arrows show how their house loses energy to the outside.

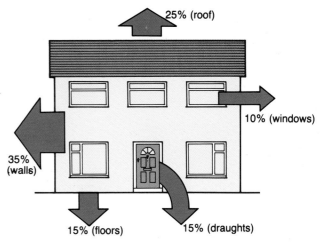

25% (roof)

10% (windows)

35% (walls)

15% (floors)   15% (draughts)

a) The Whites decided to insulate their roof. The insulation cost £150 and they found that their fuel bills were £50 cheaper each year.
How long will it take for the fuel savings to pay for the cost of insulating the roof?

b) Pleased with the roof insulation, the Whites had the cavity walls of their house filled with foam. This cost £900 and their fuel bills went down by £150 per year.

i) What is a cavity wall?

ii) How does the foam reduce heat loss?

iii) How long will it take for the fuel savings to pay for the cost of the cavity wall insulation?

c) Finally the Whites had all their old windows replaced by double-glazing units. This cost £3000. Their fuel bills went down by £50 per year.

i) What is double-glazing?

ii) How long will it take for the fuel savings to pay for the double-glazing?

iii) The Whites' house is near a busy road. Suggest one reason why they are very happy with their double-glazing.

5 a) What is meant by the term 'fossil fuel'?

b) Explain why scientists are trying to find alternative energy sources now.

c) Describe one alternative source of energy that may be producing electricity for your home in the year 2055.

What causes static electricity?
What happens in electrical circuits?
How do we use electrical circuits?
What is 'mains' electricity?

In our modern society we depend on electrical devices to do work for us. The photographs show some of the electrical appliances which we use in our homes. Each one converts electrical energy into another form.

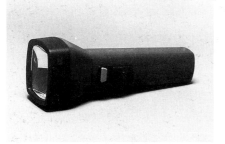

Converts electrical energy into light

Converts electrical energy into heat

Converts electrical energy into kinetic energy and heat

Converts electrical energy into sound

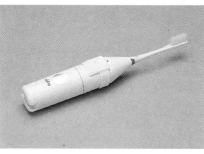

Converts electrical energy into kinetic energy

Converts electrical energy into light (and heat)

Notice that each appliance needs to be connected to a power supply. Some contain batteries. Others must be plugged into a socket connected to the mains supply.

WARNING

Remember that it is never safe to experiment with electrical circuits connected to the mains supply. Electric shocks can kill!

At home you can experiment safely with the type of 'battery' used in torches and bicycle lamps.

In the laboratory you may use a low voltage power supply or transformer which plugs into the mains. Always follow the teacher's instructions.

Activities

1 List all the electrical appliances in your home. For each one, state whether it uses batteries or is mains operated. Also write down the type, or types, of energy 'produced' by the appliance.

A table like the one below will help you to set out your answer.

appliance	mains or battery?	converts electrical energy to ...
table lamp	mains	light (and heat)

2 What would life be like if we did not understand how to use electricity? Write some notes showing what you think the main changes would be. In particular think of home, transport, and communications.

Electrostatics

Lightning is nature's most spectacular demonstration of **static electricity**. The same effect can be seen on a smaller scale when a nylon jumper is taken off; crackling can be heard and, in a dark room, small sparks can be seen. There are lots of tricks you can do to demonstrate static electricity, and it also has some very important applications.

The effects of static electricity are referred to as **electrostatics**.

Lightning is the result of a build-up of static electricity in the atmosphere.

Activities

1 Rub a plastic ruler with a dry cloth and then hold it just above some small pieces of paper. The paper will be attracted to the ruler.

2 Rub an inflated rubber balloon on a woollen jumper and then hold it against a wall. The balloon may stick to the wall.

3 Turn on a tap so that a thin, steady stream of water runs into the sink. Rub a plastic pen vigorously on a piece of material and then hold it close to the stream of water. The water will be attracted towards the pen.

These activities show that insulating materials like plastic, rubber, and glass become charged with electricity when they are rubbed. They can then attract other objects.

Other experiments show that there are two types of electrical charge: positive (+) and negative (−). When rubbed, some materials like polyethene become negatively charged. Others, like Perspex, become positively charged.

Electrostatic forces

The forces between two charged plastic rods can be studied by hanging one from an insulating thread and bringing the other close to it.

The results of the experiment can be written as:

- **Like charges repel, unlike charges attract.**

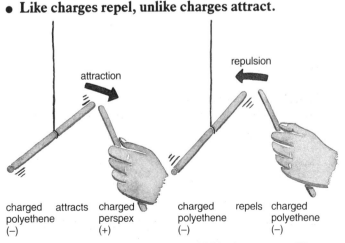

charged polyethene (−) attracts charged perspex (+)

charged polyethene (−) repels charged polyethene (−)

There is a force between two charged objects. Unlike charges attract; like charges repel.

A theory for static electricity

All materials are made up of **atoms**. The diagram shows a model of an atom. In the nucleus there are particles called **protons**. These carry a positive charge. Around the nucleus are particles called **electrons**. These carry a negative charge. (There are only two types of charge.) Atoms are **neutral**. They have equal numbers of negative electrons and positive protons.

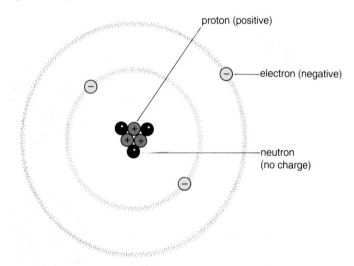

In this model of the atom there are two types of charged particle: electrons (−) and protons (+). Neutral objects contain equal numbers of positive and negative charges.

Rubbing a material with a cloth can pull away electrons. This leaves the material positively charged.

Sometimes the material pulls electrons from the cloth. This gives it a negative charge. Notice that it is always the electrons which move. This is because they are much lighter than protons.

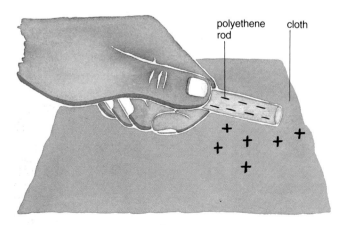

As the polyethene rod is rubbed, some electrons are pulled from the cloth. The rod becomes negatively charged . . . and the cloth becomes positively charged.

Using the theory

Example 1. A charged plastic rod can pick up a neutral piece of paper. This is because the charges on the rod separate some of the charges in the paper. Notice that this does not make any new charge. It just makes some electrons move closer, leaving unbalanced charges behind.

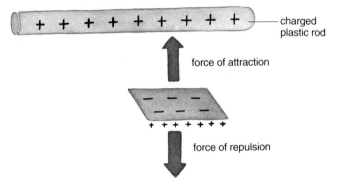

Example 2. In a warm, dry room with a nylon carpet, you may get an electric shock when touching a metal filing cabinet or a door handle. Friction between your shoes and the carpet charges you, as shown in the diagram. When you touch the door handle the charge can flow through the door to Earth. (*Note:* the Earth is so large it can take excess electrons or supply them without becoming charged.)

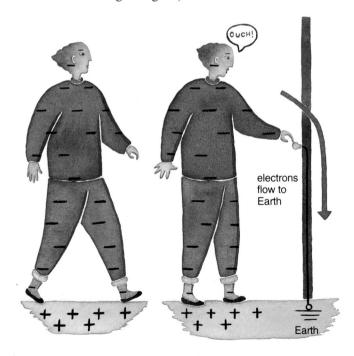

Person (and carpet) charged by friction

Person feels shock as charge flows to Earth as a current

Electrostatics has many important applications. Some of them are given here.

Electrostatic precipitation

Steel-making, producing electricity at coal-fired power stations, cement-making, and other industrial processes make smoke. The smoke which leaves factory chimneys contains small particles of ash and other solids suspended in the hot gases. When this ash is breathed in it can cause health problems. It can also pollute the environment by blackening buildings. One way of removing the dust is to use an **electrostatic precipitator**.

As the smoke and gases go up the chimney they pass wires at very high negative voltages of about 50 000 V. This causes electrons to be formed which start to move towards the earthed sides of the chimney. On the way, these charge up dust particles. The charged dust particles collect on the sides of the chimney. Every so often the chimney is given a sharp blow by a mechanical hammer so that the dust drops down into a large box for collection and disposal. In a power station up to 50 tonnes of dust can be collected in one hour!

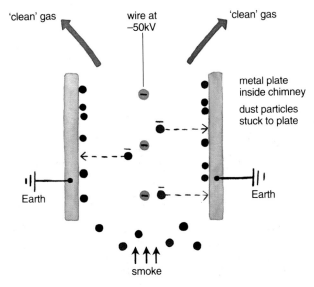

The wires at −50 kV charge up the dust particles in the smoke. These then move across to the earthed metal plates. Clean gases leave the chimney.

Photocopying

Photocopiers contain a drum coated with a material called selenium. This can be charged up, but it loses its charge in bright light. In the copier, a bright light reflects from the paper and an image is formed on the drum. The black parts of the image keep their charge but the white parts become neutral. Fine carbon dust (called **toner**) is blown on to the drum, but only sticks to the charged parts. A piece of paper is then pressed on to the drum, picking up the carbon dust pattern. The paper then passes through a heater where the toner is baked on.

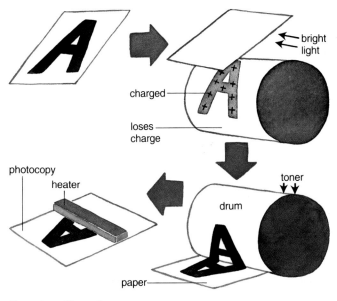

Stages in making a photocopy

Paint spraying

Paint spraying gives a high-quality, even finish to metal surfaces. Cars are sprayed with several layers of paint during their manufacture. However, paint spraying is messy and much of the paint is wasted. The quality and efficiency of spray painting can be improved by charging the paint droplets in the spray and charging the metal objects with the opposite charge. This attracts the paint droplets on to the charged surface.

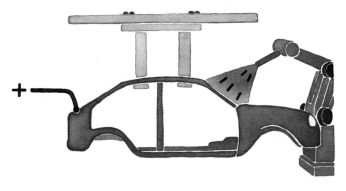

Using electrostatics to make paint spraying more efficient

Currents and circuits

All materials contain atoms. Atoms in turn contain small, electrically charged particles called electrons and ions. The diagrams show one way of thinking about these particles.

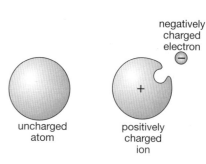

An electrical circuit is a pathway which charged particles can move along. For example, the diagram opposite shows a simple circuit for lighting a bulb. The circuit contains a battery. We think of the battery as 'pushing' the charge around the circuit. It is connected to the bulb by wires made of metal. The metal is a **conductor**; conductors let charge pass along them. Look at the circuit and you will see that there is a complete path from the positive end of the battery to the bulb, through the bulb and back to the negative end of the battery.

An electrical circuit must have a complete conducting pathway. If there are any gaps, the charge cannot flow.

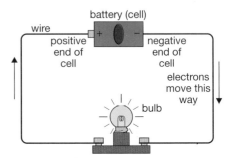

Switches

Switches are used to control electrical circuits.

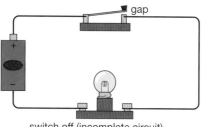

switch off (incomplete circuit)

The bulb does not light up.

*There is a gap in the circuit which will not conduct electricity. (Air is an **insulator**.)*

*We say that the switch is **open** or **off**.*

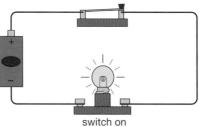

switch on
(complete circuit)

The bulb does light up.

The metal switch conducts electricity and so the circuit is complete.

*We say that the switch is **closed** or **on**.*

Questions

1 In the circuits opposite the wires are made of *copper* and are covered with *plastic*. The filament inside the bulb is made of *tungsten*. The switch has *brass* contacts and a *wooden* base.
For each of the five materials listed, state whether it is a conductor or an insulator.

2 Electric wires must be insulated. Some people insulate their houses. What is the difference between an *electrical insulator* and a *thermal insulator*?

Circuit diagrams

It is not convenient to draw pictures of electrical components all the time. Also, if you are a bad artist, other people may not understand your diagrams! Scientists and electrical engineers use **symbols** to represent the parts of an electrical circuit. The diagram opposite uses some of the standard symbols.

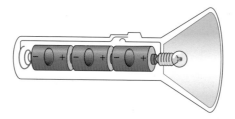

This drawing shows the inside of a torch.

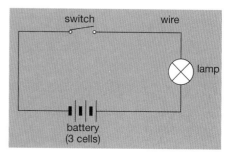

This is the circuit diagram for the torch.

Measuring currents

In a circuit containing a light bulb, we can judge the size of the current by looking at the brightness of the bulb. A large current makes the bulb glow brightly. A small current makes the bulb glow dimly or not at all. This method is not accurate enough for scientific work so a meter, called an **ammeter**, is used to measure the current.

The size of the current is measured in units called **amperes**. We nearly always shorten this to **amps** (symbol A).

When an ammeter is used it is connected **in** the circuit. It measures the current flowing through it.

An ammeter

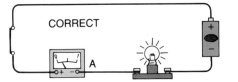

Here the meter is connected in the circuit. It measures the current in the lamp.

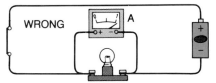

Here the meter is not connected in the main circuit. It does not measure the current in the lamp. The meter may be damaged.

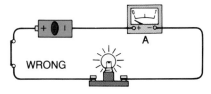

Here the meter is connected the wrong way around. The pointer moves the wrong way. The meter may be damaged.

What is an ampere?

The size of a current shows us how much charge flows through the circuit in one second. The unit of charge is the **coulomb** (symbol C).

A current of 1 A means that 1 C of charge flows in each second. (In fact each electron carries only a very small charge. About six million million million electrons are needed to give a charge of 1 coulomb!)

Sample question

What is the current in the circuit opposite?
Answer 2 A (Read the meter!)

How much charge flows through the lamp in one second?
Answer 2 C (1 A means 1 C in each second so 2 A means 2 C in each second.)

How much charge flows through the lamp in 10 s?
Answer 20 C (2 A means 2 C in each second so in 10 s we have 2 × 10 C.)

Hint: If you multiply the current (I) by the time (t) your answer is the charge (Q). In mathematical language ... $Q = I \times t$.

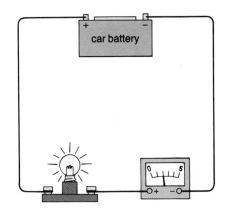

Questions

1 The diagram (right) shows an ammeter scale. What is the current when the pointer is at
a) A **b)** B **c)** C?

2 When the pointer is at B, how much charge flows through the ammeter in **a)** 1 s **b)** 10 s **c)** 60 s?

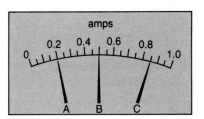

In the simplest circuits, all the components are joined together in one 'pathway'. There are no branches or junctions. These are called **series circuits**.

This picture shows a cell (battery), a switch and two lamps connected in series.

When the switch is closed, both lamps light. The switch controls both lamps.

If one of the bulbs 'blows' the circuit is broken. The other lamp goes out.

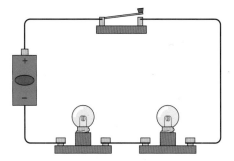

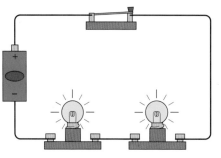

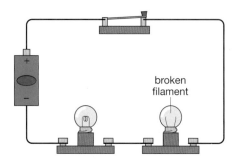

broken filament

Current in a series circuit

The current is the same at all places in a series circuit. This is because the current only has one pathway to flow through. It has to pass through all the components.

The diagram shows two cells, two identical lamps, and four ammeters connected in series. Notice that all the ammeters show the same value. The bulbs will light with equal brightness.

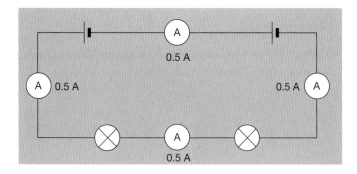

Adding more components

Adding more cells in a series circuit will 'push' more current around it. Any bulbs in the circuit will be brighter.

Adding more bulbs or other components will make it more difficult for current to flow.

In this circuit, one cell can make a current of 0.4 A flow through one bulb.

Here an extra cell has been added. Now there is more current and the bulb glows more brightly.

Here one cell is pushing current through two bulbs. The current is only 0.2 A and the bulbs merely glow dimly.

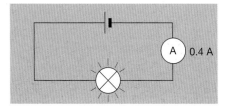

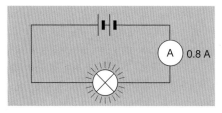

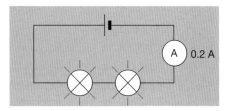

Parallel circuits

Circuits which have junctions where the electrical pathway divides or branches are called **parallel circuits**.

This picture shows a circuit with two lamps connected in parallel.

When the switch is closed, both lamps light. The switch, in this position, controls both lamps.

If one of the bulbs 'blows' the other lamp stays on. There is still a complete circuit through the undamaged bulb.

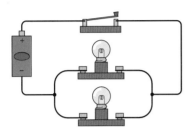
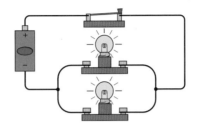
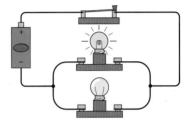

Switches in parallel circuits

Switches in parallel circuits can control the whole circuit, or just part of the circuit. This can be very useful.

In the diagram opposite, switch A controls all the bulbs. Switch B only controls bulb 1. Switch C only controls bulbs 2 and 3.

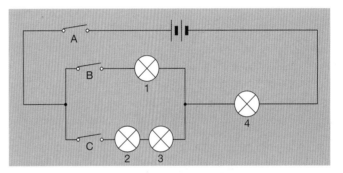

Current in a parallel circuit

The current is not the same at all places in the parallel circuit. This is because the current 'splits' at the junction in the circuit. Different currents can flow in parallel pathways. They then join up again.

The diagram shows a parallel circuit. Notice that the current flowing through the 'two bulb' section is less than that flowing in the other, parallel pathway.

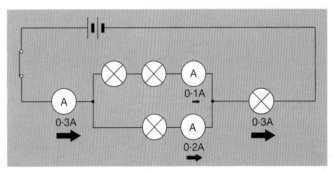

Questions

1 The car shown opposite has two headlamp bulbs and two rear light bulbs connected in parallel with the car's 12 V battery.

   a) Draw a circuit diagram to show how the four bulbs are connected to the battery. Include in your circuit one switch which would control all the bulbs.

   b) Use your diagram to explain why if one bulb 'blows', the other three stay on.

   c) Each headlamp draws a current of 3 A and each rear light bulb draws 0.5 A. What is the total current drawn from the car battery?

   d) A car battery can give a current of 1 A for about 35 hours. A driver leaves the car parked with the lights on. Estimate how long it will be before the battery is 'flat'.

All electrical circuits need a source of energy. The photographs show some of the supplies you may meet. Each of these provides the **voltage** or **potential difference** needed to make a current flow in a circuit. (It may help if you think of the voltage as being the 'push' which makes charge flow.)

*A normal dry cell gives about 1.5 V. A number of cells can be joined together to make a **battery** which gives a bigger voltage.*

A lead-acid cell gives about 2 V. A car battery uses six cells to give a total of 12 V between its terminals.

This laboratory supply plugs into the mains. It gives a low voltage (up to 12 V) from its terminals.

Measuring voltage

Voltage or potential difference can be measured using a voltmeter.

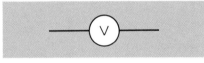

symbol

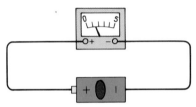

Here a voltmeter is connected across one dry cell. It reads 1.5 V (volts).

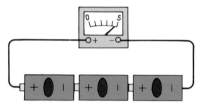

Here the voltmeter is across a battery of three cells. It shows that there is a voltage of 4.5 V.

Unlike ammeters, voltmeters are **not** connected in the main circuit. They are added **across** the component where we want to find the voltage.

Like ammeters, the voltmeters must be connected the right way around. If not, the pointer moves the wrong way and the meter may be damaged.

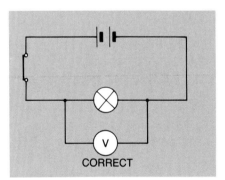

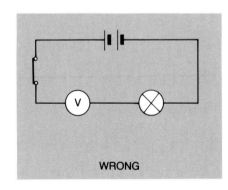

Voltages around a circuit

The battery or power supply provides the total voltage for the circuit. In a simple circuit, the voltages across all the components add up to the supply voltage.

The circuits opposite show how the voltage is 'shared out' when all the components, in this case lamps, are identical.

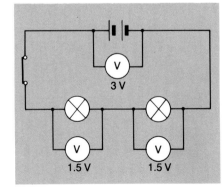

1 V + 1 V + 1 V = 3 V

1.5 V + 1.5 V = 3 V

Voltage, current, and resistance

In a circuit the power supply provides the voltage which makes the current flow. Larger voltages cause larger currents.

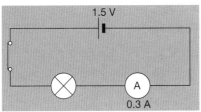

In this circuit 1.5 V gives a current of 0.3 A.

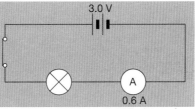

Twice as much voltage (3.0 V) gives twice as much current (0.6 A).

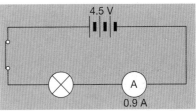

Three times the voltage (4.5 V) gives three times the current (0.9 A).

A battery does not always give the same current. It depends on what is in the circuit connected to it. Some components allow electricity to pass 'easily'. We say that these have **low resistance**. Other components make it 'hard' for current to flow. We say that these have **high resistance**.

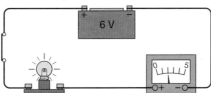

When connected to a 6 V battery, this lamp allows a current of 2 A.

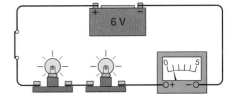

When two of these lamps are connected the resistance is higher and so the current is about 1 A.

Resistances and wires

The wires used for connecting up circuits in the laboratory or in the home have very low resistance. This is because they are made of copper; a metal which is a very good conductor.

The resistance of any wire depends on three main things: its **length**, its **diameter** or **area**, and the **material** from which it is made.

Long wires have higher resistances than short wires.

Thin wires have higher resistances than thick wires.

The resistance of a wire depends on the material used.

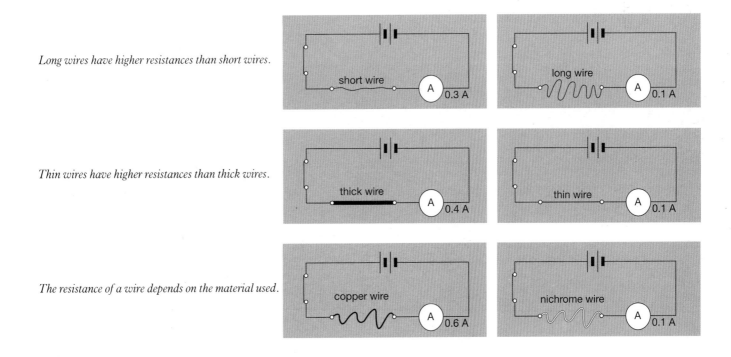

Measuring resistance

The resistance of a component or a circuit tells us how many volts we need to apply to make a current of 1 A flow. If a circuit has a large resistance we have to apply a high voltage to get a current of 1 A to flow. If the circuit has a low resistance only a small voltage is needed.

Resistance is measured in units called **ohms**. The symbol for the ohm is Ω (the Greek letter 'omega').

1 V is needed to make a current of 1 A flow through a resistance of 1 Ω.

The table opposite shows the pattern between voltage, current and resistance.

The diagram opposite shows a circuit to measure the resistance of a piece of wire.

The voltmeter is measuring the voltage **across** the wire and the ammeter is measuring the current **in** the wire.

To find the resistance we just divide the voltage by the current.

voltage		resistance		current
1 V	across	1 Ω	gives	1 A
2 V	across	1 Ω	gives	2 A
1 V	across	2 Ω	gives	$\frac{1}{2}$ A
2 V	across	2 Ω	gives	1 A
6 V	across	2 Ω	gives	3 A

The rule is VOLTAGE = CURRENT $\times$ RESISTANCE
in symbols $\qquad V = I R$

or $\qquad \dfrac{\text{VOLTAGE}}{\text{CURRENT}} = \text{RESISTANCE} \qquad \dfrac{V}{I} = R$

This is Ohm's law

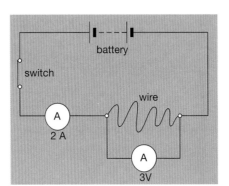

Calculation
Voltmeter reading = 3 V
Ammeter reading = 2 A

$$\text{resistance} = \frac{\text{voltage}}{\text{current}}$$

$$\text{resistance} = \frac{3\,\text{V}}{2\,\text{A}} = 1.5\,\Omega$$

The resistance of the wire is 1.5 Ω.

Questions

1 The diagram shows the circuit set up by a boy trying to measure the resistance of a light bulb. He has made several mistakes. What are they? Draw the correct circuit.

2 When the circuit is set up correctly, it is found that a voltage of 3 V gives a current of 0.5 A.
What voltage would be needed to give a current of 1 A?
What is the resistance of the bulb in the circuit?

3 A girl uses the apparatus to measure the resistance of a copper connecting wire. She finds that 0.1 V (one tenth of a volt) gives a current of 1 A.
  a) What is the resistance of the copper wire?
  b) Why is the girl's value for the resistance likely to be inaccurate? (*Hint*: think of the voltmeter scale!)

Controlling the current

When we need to control the current in a circuit, we can use a **resistor**. The diagram shows a resistor and its standard symbol.

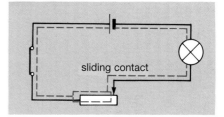

resistor

symbol for a resistor

The circuit opposite shows a resistor being used to protect a lamp which would 'blow' if connected directly to the battery. Having extra resistance in the circuit limits the current.

lamp

resistor

It is often useful to be able to change the current in a circuit. This can be done by using a **variable resistor**. The photograph shows one with a sliding contact being used. As the contact is moved, the length of the resistance wire connected in the circuit changes and so the current changes.

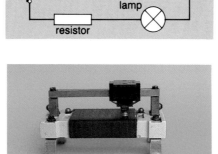

A variable resistor with a sliding contact.

sliding contact

A **perfect** resistor always has the same resistance. The diagram shows a circuit used to see how the current through a resistor changes as the voltage across it is changed. The results are shown in the table and also on the graph below.

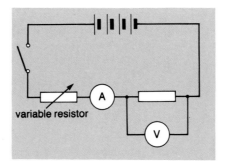

variable resistor

voltage across resistor	current in resistor
0 V	0.0 A
1 V	0.2 A
2 V	0.4 A
3 V	0.6 A
4 V	0.8 A

Notice that as the voltage doubles from 1 V to 2 V, the current doubles from 0.2 A to 0.4 A. Then as the voltage doubles again (2 V to 4 V) the current doubles (0.4 to 0.8). We say that **the current is proportional to the voltage**.

Questions

1) Using the graph, find:
   a) The current in the resistor when the voltage across it is 1.5 V.
   b) The voltage that gives a current of 0.5 A.
   c) The voltage that would give a current of 1 A.

2) Explain why it would not be sensible to use the graph to predict what will happen when a voltage of 230 V is applied to the resistor.

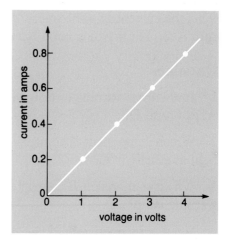

Current-voltage relation for a resistor.

More electrical components

There are many other components that we can use in our circuits.

Component and symbol	What it does
LED (light-emitting diode)	These are small lamps used in electronic circuits. They give a bright light when a small current flows. Red LEDs are common but you can also get green and yellow ones. They are used as indicator lamps in many electronic devices. They are also used in 'flashing' bike lamps.
LDR (light-dependent resistor)	The resistance of an LDR changes with light intensity. In bright light it has a low resistance. In the dark it has a high resistance. LDRs are used in circuits controlled by light e.g. automatic street lamps.
Thermistor	The resistance of a thermistor changes with temperature. Most thermistors have a high resistance when cold and a lower resistance when warm. Thermistors are used in circuits controlled by temperature e.g. fire alarms, frost warning devices.
Transistor	A transistor is a small, electronically controlled switch. Integrated circuits (ICs) contain many transistors on a single 'chip'. Transistors and ICs are used in computers, communication devices, and car control systems.

This is a frost warning device. As the temperature falls, the resistance of the thermistor increases. At 0 °C, the current into the transistor is big enough to turn it on. The warning lamp lights up.

Questions

1   In the frost warning circuit, what are components A, B, C and D?

2   Which component is adjusted to make the lamp light at exactly 0 °C?

3   Why is component B connected to the warning lamp?

4   What component would you use in place of the thermistor to make a light-sensitive switch?

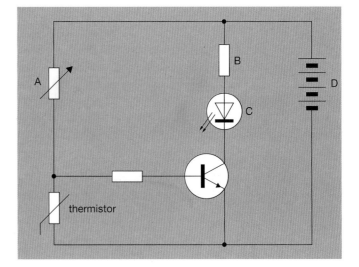

Frost warning device.

Switches and control

Switches control electrical circuits. Switches connected together are called **logic gates**. They only let information through if the correct combination of switches is closed. We can think of gates as making decisions.

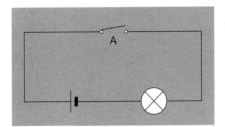

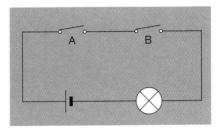

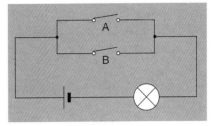

This switch is controlling the lamp in the circuit. When the switch is closed, the lamp is on. When the switch is open, the lamp is off.

In this arrangement, the two switches are in series. The lamp is only on if switch A **AND** switch B are closed. This is an **AND** gate.

Here the switches are in parallel. The lamp will come on if either switch A **OR** switch B is closed. (It will also come on if both are closed.) This is an **OR** gate.

We can show the action of logic gates using **truth tables**. A truth table shows all possible combinations of inputs and outputs.

If a switch is open, the **input** is low or 0. If a switch is closed the input is high or 1.

If the lamp is off, the **output** is low or 0. If the lamp is on, the output is high or 1.

AND gate truth table

A	B	C
0	0	0
0	1	0
1	0	0
1	1	1

OR gate truth table

A	B	C
0	0	0
0	1	1
1	0	1
1	1	1

AND gate symbol

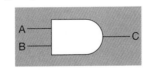

OR gate symbol

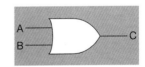

Electronic control circuits use integrated circuits or 'chips' which have many electronic logic gates packaged in one component. Connections are made to the gates through the small metal 'legs'.

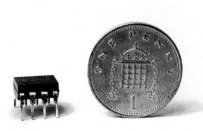

This integrated circuit 'chip' contains many transistor circuits.

Logic gates in control

Logic gate inputs can be connected to sensors. The gate will then only give an output when conditions from the sensors are 'correct'. This is very important for control. A simple example is shown opposite. It is an electronically operated lock which needs two keys to open it. Each key, when turned, gives a high input signal ('1'). If a high output signal is sent to the coil of the lock the door can be opened. The lock only opens when keys are turned in locks A AND B.

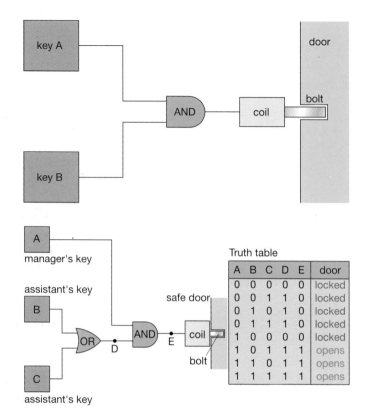

Now consider this; a bank manager has one key to the bank's safe. Each of the bank's two assistant managers also has a key. The manager wants to make sure that the safe is never opened unless he is there with at least one of his assistants. The circuit opposite could be used. The OR gate gives an output of '1' when key B OR C is turned. Now when the manager's key, A, is turned the AND gate gives an output of '1' to open the lock.

We can use logic gates to automatically control circuits. We connect one of the inputs to a **sensor**.

Truth table

A	B	C	D	E	door
0	0	0	0	0	locked
0	0	1	1	0	locked
0	1	0	1	0	locked
0	1	1	1	0	locked
1	0	0	0	0	locked
1	0	1	1	1	opens
1	1	0	1	1	opens
1	1	1	1	1	opens

Parking light circuit

Input A of the AND gate is always high because it is connected to the 6 V wire. When it is dark the resistance of the LDR is high and so input B is at a high level. The truth table shows us that when A AND B are high the output is high. This allows a small current to flow in the coil of the relay turning the light bulb on. When it is light the resistance of the LDR is low and so input B is low. The AND gate then gives a low output and the lamp turns off.

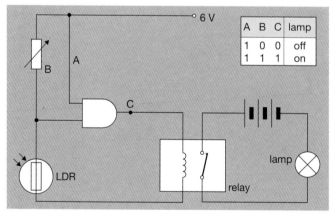

A	B	C	lamp
1	0	0	off
1	1	1	on

Automatic lighting circuit

Question

1 This device is designed to make an LED light up when the temperature rises above 100 °C.

    a) What logic gate is being used?

    b) What is the truth table for this logic gate?

    c) What happens to the thermistor when the temperature rises?

    d) What happens to the input level at B when the temperature reaches 100 °C?

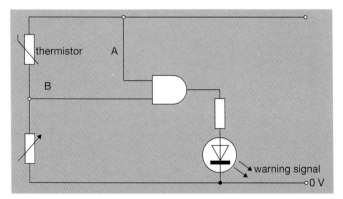

High temperature warning device

Electricity in the home

Many of the electrical appliances in our homes plug into sockets connected to the mains supply. Mains electricity is produced at power stations by the electricity generating board. It is then sent along power lines to houses, factories, hospitals, schools and other users.

There are two important differences between using the mains as a supply and using a battery:

1 The type of cell or battery used in a torch gives a voltage of about 1.5 V. Mains electricity is at about 230 V!

The mains can also supply very large currents. It is dangerous to touch wires connected to the mains supply. **An electric shock could kill you**.

2 A battery gives a steady voltage and so when it is connected in a circuit the electricity always flows in the same direction. This is **direct current** or d.c.

The mains voltage changes direction very rapidly. This makes the current flow backwards and forwards 50 times in each second. We say that this is an **alternating current** or a.c. with a frequency of 50 Hz. (Hz stands for hertz. 1 Hz is 1 cycle per second.)

The electricity board supplies two wires to your home. One is called the **live** and the other is the **neutral**. The live wire is at about 230 V and the neutral wire is at about 0 V. Electrical circuits in your home are connected to these wires.

This oscilloscope shows the steady voltage from a battery.

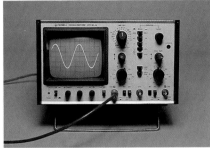
This oscilloscope shows how the voltage of the mains supply varies with time.

Why is this dangerous?

Why doesn't this person feel an electric shock?

The Electricity Board's mains supply

Activities

1 Find where the Electricity Board's supply enters your home. If you do not know where this is, ask someone to show you the electricity meter.
See if you can find two thick wires going into the bottom of the meter. One may have red insulation; this is the live wire. The other may have black insulation; this is the neutral wire. **Do not touch these**.

2 Look at a torch bulb and see if you can find its voltage rating. (The value is usually printed on the metal base.) See if you can find the voltage rating of a mains light bulb. (It is usually printed on the top of the glass.)

The ring-main

A light bulb draws less than 0.5 A from the mains supply so the lighting circuit in a house is designed to carry a maximum current of about 5 A. Electric heaters, kettles, and irons take much bigger currents and so must not be connected to the lighting circuit in case they cause overheating. They are connected to separate mains circuits by using plugs in sockets. The sockets in modern houses are connected in a circuit called a **ring-main**.

You should be able to see from the diagram why it is called a ring-main: there is a loop of wire from the live side of the supply right around the house and back again. Similarly there is a ring of wire from the neutral side. Sockets are connected to this loop.

One terminal is joined to the live wire and so is at about 230 V. Another terminal is joined to the neutral wire and so is at 0 V.

Notice that the ring-main has an extra wire. This is called the **earth** wire and is there for safety. How it works is explained later in this chapter.

Adding an extra socket

Extra sockets can be connected to the ring main using a **spur**. The diagram shows how the extra socket is connected. Notice that each socket in the ring-main is connected to the mains supply by two pathways; one around each side of the ring. The spur just uses a single pathway.

Plugs

Appliances are connected to the mains using plugs which have three pins. The longer pin, at the top, makes a connection to the earth wire. As it is pushed in it opens the lower holes in the socket so that its shorter pins can connect with the live and neutral wires.

It is very dangerous to push anything other than a proper plug into a mains socket!

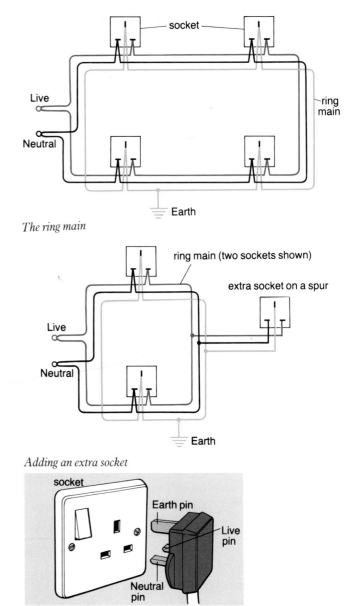

The ring main

Adding an extra socket

The live and neutral holes are usually covered up for safety. When the long, earth pin is pushed in, the covers are pushed aside so that the neutral and live pins can make contact. It is very dangerous to push anything other than a plug into a mains socket.

Questions

1 The wires used in lighting circuits are thinner than those used in ring-mains. Suggest why this is.

2 Are the sockets in a ring-main connected in series or parallel? Explain your answer.

3 One light bulb draws a current of 0.4 A from the mains supply. A house has eight light bulbs connected to one of its circuits. When all the lights are turned on, what will be the total current drawn from the mains?

Lighting circuits

The lights in a house are usually connected in a **loop** circuit. All the lamps are connected in parallel. Each bulb is connected to the neutral wire on one side and, through a switch, to the live wire on the other. When the switch is closed a bulb has about 230 V across it. This makes a current flow and so the bulb lights.

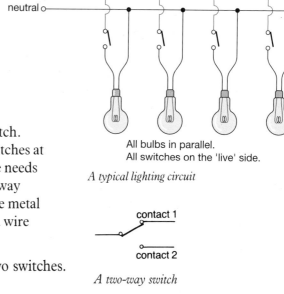

All bulbs in parallel.
All switches on the 'live' side.

A typical lighting circuit

Two-way switching

In the simple lighting circuit, each bulb is controlled by one switch. Sometimes we want to be able to turn a light on and off from switches at two different places. For example, a light at the top of a staircase needs switches at the top and bottom of the stairs. These must be two-way switches. The circuit symbol for a two-way switch shows that the metal conductor moves between two contacts. Each contact can have a wire connected to it.

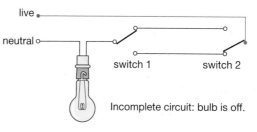

A two-way switch

The circuits below show one light bulb being controlled by two switches.

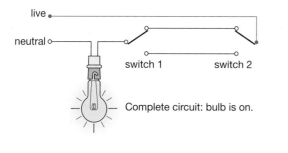

Complete circuit: bulb on

Incomplete circuit: bulb off

Light switches in bathrooms

The type of switch used in a living room would be dangerous in a bathroom. If used with wet hands the water could get behind the switch cover and make a conducting pathway between the live wire and the person. This could give a fatal shock. Pull-switches like the one shown are much safer.

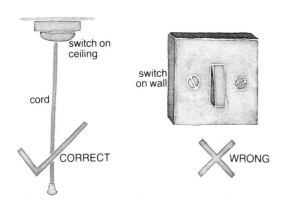

Activities

Carry out a survey in your home to answer these questions:

1 How many light bulbs are used in your home?

2 How many lights are controlled by two-way switches?

3 Why are two-way switches useful **a)** on staircases, and **b)** in bedrooms?

4 Is the switch in your bathroom a pull-switch? Are there any other rooms in your home where pull-switches are used?

5 Are the light switches in your other rooms made of plastic or metal? Older houses sometimes have brass light switches. Why are plastic ones safer?

Safety and electricity

Our homes would be less comfortable without mains electricity and life would be much harder. However, mains electricity can be dangerous if it is not handled correctly. To prevent damage to property and danger to life the circuits in your home have built in safety measures.

Fuses

When wires carry an electric current they get warm. If the current is too large the wires can get hot enough to start a fire. One way of preventing this is to put a fuse in all the circuits in the home. These are put in the **live** wire close to the electricity meter in a box called the **consumer unit**.

Each fuse contains a thin piece of wire made from a mixture of metals which will melt at a low temperature. If the current gets too high, the fuse wire melts and leaves a gap in the circuit. This stops the current.

Fuses and switches are always connected in the live wire; never in the neutral wire. This is so that they can be used to disconnect the appliance from the 230 V wire. A fuse or switch placed in the neutral wire would work and would stop the current but someone touching the appliance could still get a shock.

When a fuse in the consumer unit 'blows' it must be replaced with one of the correct size. Some can have a new piece of fuse wire fitted but this too must be of the correct rating; 5 A for lighting, 30 A for ring-mains and 45 A for cooker circuits. **It is very dangerous to use anything other than the correct fuse wire**. If a piece of ordinary copper wire is used it will let very large currents flow and may allow a fire to start.

This consumer unit is fitted with fuses. These protect the home's circuits.

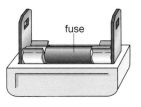

Fuse carrier with cartridge fuse

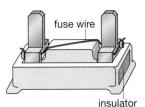

Fuse carrier with fuse wire (designs may vary)

Miniature circuit breakers

Replacing a fuse or a piece of fuse wire is not easy particularly if all the lights have gone out! Some houses have their circuits protected by small electromagnetic switches called **miniature circuit breakers** or mcb's for short. Normally the switch of the mcb is pushed in to complete the circuit. However, if the current gets too high, the switch springs out breaking the circuit. Once the reason for the circuit overload has been found the switch of the mcb can just be pushed back in until it clicks into place.

Miniature circuit breakers, just like fuses, have to operate at different currents. A 5 A circuit breaker is used to protect the lighting circuit and a 30 A mcb protects the ring-main.

Miniature circuit breakers

Wiring a plug

In Britain, appliances are connected to the ring main using three-pin plugs. The standard plug has square pins; two short pins and one longer one. The wires and pins must always be connected in the same way. To help, the wires in the connecting lead are colour coded. The code should be remembered;

brown = live　　　**blue = neutral**　　　**green/yellow = earth**

The tools needed to wire a plug are a small screwdriver with an insulating handle, wire-strippers and a sharp knife.

Step 1 *Unscrew the large screw which is between the pins of the plug. Remove the lid.*

Step 2 *Loosen the cable clamp by undoing the small screws. It is a good idea to take one screw out completely. Take the fuse out of the plug. This will make wiring the plug easier.*

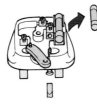

Step 3 *Using a sharp knife, make a slit about 4 cm long in the outer covering of the cable. Pull the wires out of the slit and then cut off the loose bit of covering. Take great care not to damage the insulation of the wires.*

Step 4 *Using wire-strippers pull about 2 cm of the insulation from each of the wires.*

Step 5 *Put the cable under the clamp. Check that each wire will reach its terminal. Do up the clamp so that it grips the cable firmly. Connect each wire to its correct terminal. Make sure that the terminal screw is tightened on to the bare wire.*

Step 6 *Check the following:*
Have you tightened the cable grip? Have you connected the wires correctly according to the colour code?
Have you tightened the terminal screws?
Have you made sure that no bare wires are touching?

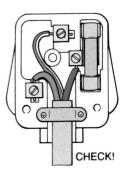

CHECK!

Step 7 *Push the fuse into the holder. Screw on the lid of the plug.*
Test the appliance by plugging it in and switching on.

Note: *the cable for some appliances does not have an earth wire. In this case the larger pin is left unconnected. The two wires must still be connected correctly: brown = live, blue = neutral.*

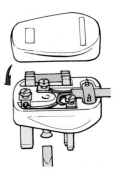

Earthing

If you touch a live wire at about 230 V an electric current can pass through your body to the ground which is at 0 V. The pain you feel is an electric shock. The small current that runs through your body may be enough to kill you even though it is too small to blow the circuit's fuse. Ring-mains and lighting circuits have an **earth wire** to protect users.

Outside each house, close to where the main electricity cables enter, a metal plate is buried in the ground. This is joined to a connector block in the consumer unit where the earth wires from all the house circuits are connected. If a fault lets the live wire become connected to the earth, a large current flows in the earth wire. This makes a fuse blow, often with a bang, cutting off the electricity supply.

Residual current circuit breakers

Sometimes a fault occurs which makes the outside of a properly earthed appliance become live but where the current in the earth wire is not enough to blow a fuse. This could be very dangerous. A residual current circuit breaker can be used to protect against this. It contains an electro-magnetic switch which quickly turns off the power if the current in the earth wire is bigger than 0.03 A. Circuit breakers like this are recommended for use with lawn mowers and portable tools like electric drills. Ask your teacher whether the school laboratories are protected by earth leakage circuit breakers.

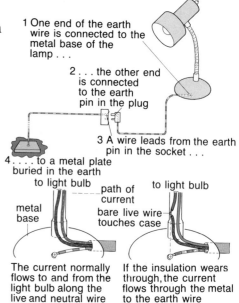

1 One end of the earth wire is connected to the metal base of the lamp . . .

2 . . . the other end is connected to the earth pin in the plug

3 A wire leads from the earth pin in the socket . . .

4 . . . to a metal plate buried in the earth

to light bulb

metal base

path of current

The current normally flows to and from the light bulb along the live and neutral wire

to light bulb

bare live wire touches case

If the insulation wears through, the current flows through the metal to the earth wire

No earth wire!

Appliances marked '**double insulated**' do not have an earth wire. This is because their metal parts are covered with insulating plastic. The live wire can never touch the casing and so cannot give the user a shock.

The diagram shows how the wires should be connected in the plug of a 'double insulated' appliance.

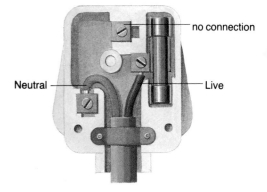

no connection

Neutral

Live

Questions

1 What colour is the insulation of the earth wire?

2 The outside of a hair dryer is made from plastic. Why doesn't it need an earth wire?

3 Explain how the earth wire **and** fuse help to prevent electric shocks in the case of accidents.

4 Why must the fuse be in the **live** wire and not the neutral wire? (*Hint*: think of the voltages of the two wires.)

5 Try to find out the correct first aid treatment for someone suffering from an electric shock.

Fuses for appliances

The main fuses in the consumer unit protect the house circuits from damage due to **overload** (too much current). Each appliance is also protected by a fuse in its plug. The diagrams opposite show the type of cartridge fuse used in mains plugs. Inside there is a thin wire made of a metal alloy which melts at a low temperature. If the current gets too great, the fuse wire melts and breaks the circuit. When this happens we say that the fuse has 'blown'.

Fuses can be bought which 'blow' at different currents. They are marked with the maximum current that they can carry for a long time.

Choosing the right fuse

The fuse used in a plug should have a current rating just big enough to let the appliance work properly. If it is rated at too high a current it could allow an overload to cause damage without melting and 'blowing'. Fuses are made in various values – 1A, 2A ... Household appliance fuses are usually chosen from the following values – 3A, 5A, 10A, 13A.

Calculating currents

Appliances are often marked with their power rating. This tells us how much electrical energy they convert in each second.

$$\textbf{electrical power} = \textbf{voltage} \times \textbf{current}$$

or in symbols: $W = VI$

This gives us a way of working out the current.

$$\text{current} = \frac{\text{power}}{\text{voltage}} \quad \text{or} \quad I = \frac{W}{V}$$

Let us try this for some household appliances where the mains supply is at 250 V. (In the United Kingdom the mains supply is at 230 V. Using 250 V in our calculations makes them much easier and does not make much difference to the answers!)

3000 W electric fire: $\text{current} = \dfrac{3000\,\text{W}}{250\,\text{V}} = 12\,\text{A}$

The next highest fuse rating is 13 A so we fit a 13 A fuse in the plug of an electric fire.

100 W table lamp: $\text{current} = \dfrac{100\,\text{W}}{250\,\text{V}} = 0.4\,\text{A}$

The next highest fuse rating is 3 A so we fit a 3 A fuse in the plug of a lamp.

Appliance	Current	Fuse
150W stereo	$\dfrac{150\text{W}}{250\text{V}} = 0.6\text{A}$	
500W food mixer	$\dfrac{500\text{W}}{250\text{V}} = 2\text{A}$	3A (RED)
850W toaster	$\dfrac{850\text{W}}{250\text{V}} = 3.4\text{A}$	
1000W iron	$\dfrac{1000\text{W}}{250\text{V}} = 4\text{A}$	5A (BLACK)
2000W kettle	$\dfrac{2000\text{W}}{250\text{V}} = 8\text{A}$	
3000W heater	$\dfrac{3000\text{W}}{250\text{V}} = 12\text{A}$	13A (BROWN)

Investigating the current at which a 1 A fuse 'blows'.

The diagram below shows apparatus which can be used to find the current which will cause 1 A fuse wire to melt. Notice that the light bulb must be able to take a current greater than 1 A or the filament may melt before the fuse wire!

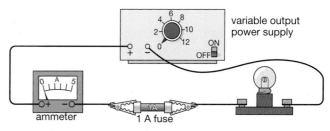

Investigating a fuse

The control on the power supply is set at **zero**. It is then gradually increased. The current rises until the fuse 'blows'. If you watch the ammeter carefully, you can record the maximum current allowed by the fuse. The maximum current is often higher than expected.

Questions

1 What is the purpose of the fuse in
  a) the consumer unit **b)** a mains plug?

2 Why would it be dangerous to use copper wire in a fuse rather than special fuse wire?

3 Suggest why fuses for use in plugs are colour coded.

4 What fuse should you fit in the plug of **a)** a 1500 W sandwich toaster **b)** a 200 W home computer?

Paying for electricity

The electricity board provides each house with a 230 V supply. When we plug an appliance into a mains socket a current flows. In the appliance, electrical energy is changed into another form. For example, a light bulb changes electrical energy into light and heat. **We pay for the energy.**

Energy is measured in units called **joules** (symbol J). The **power** of an electric appliance tells us how many joules of energy it converts in one second. The power is measured in units called **watts** (symbol W).

1 W is 1 J in each second. So, for example, a 100 W light bulb converts 100 J of energy in each second. The power of an appliance used for heating is likely to be much higher and may be measured in **kilowatts** (symbol kW). Remember that 1 kW = 1000 W.

Activities

Try to find the power of the following household appliances: (the easiest way is to use a mail order catalogue) an electric cooker, an electric kettle, an iron, a tumble dryer, a toaster, a vacuum cleaner, an electric drill, a stereo music system and a table lamp.

What do you notice about the power of appliances which contain a heating element compared with the power of those used to produce sound or light?

The longer an appliance is turned on, the more energy it will 'use'. A 1 kW heater switched on for one hour will use 3 600 000 J of energy! (1000 W × 3600 s.) Such numbers are very difficult to work with so the electricity board calculates the energy used in 'units' called kilowatt hours (symbol kW h).

A 1 kW appliance turned on for 1 h will convert 1 kW h of energy. 1 kWh of energy costs between 6p and 7p.

It is easy to work out how much an appliance costs to use:

first   **energy used = power × time**
               (kW h)   (kW)   (h)

then   **cost = energy used × cost of 1 kW h**

This 1 kW electric fire 'uses' 1000 J of energy in each second

The table below shows roughly how long one unit of electricity will last when using different appliances.

appliance	time to use 1 unit (approximate)
fan heater	$\frac{1}{2}$ hour
steam iron	1 hour
hair dryer	2 hours
power drill	4 hours
colour television	7 hours
freezer	12 hours
table lamp	15 hours

Sample questions

1   If 1 kW h of energy costs 6p, how much does it cost to use a 2 kW heater for 4 hours?

$$\text{energy used} = 2\,\text{kW} \times 4\,\text{h} = 8\,\text{kW h}$$
$$\text{cost} = (8 \times 6)\text{p} = 48\,\text{p}$$

The heater costs 48p to use for 4 hours.

This calculation only works if you remember to use the power in kilowatts and the time in hours!

2   If 1 kW h of energy costs 6p, how much does it cost to use a 100 W light bulb for 5 hours?

$$\text{energy used} = 0.1\,\text{kW} \times 5\,\text{h} = 0.5\,\text{kW h}$$
$$\text{cost} = (0.5 \times 6)\text{p} = 3\text{p}$$

The light bulb costs 3p for 5 hours use.

1 A student uses the apparatus below to test whether materials are electrical conductors or insulators. The material is connected to clips **X** and **Y**.

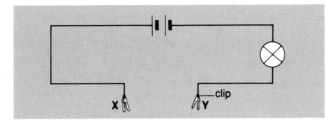

a) What is a conductor?
b) Which of the following would make the bulb light if they were connected between **X** and **Y**; iron wire, glass rod, polythene (plastic), rubber, aluminum foil?
c) When the student puts some copper wire between **X** and **Y** the bulb does not light. Suggest what might be wrong with the apparatus. How could the student check?

2 a) A student connects a bulb rated at 3 V to three 1.5 V cells as shown below.

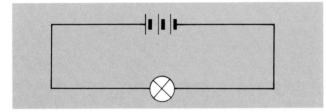

The bulb gives a bright flash and then goes out. Explain why this is.
b) The student then connects a new bulb in the circuit below.

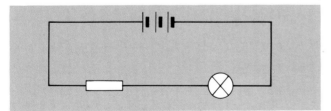

The bulb glows brightly and stays on.
i) What component has the student added?
ii) How does the new component protect the bulb?

3 A science teacher does not have enough variable resistors for a class practical so she uses the apparatus below.

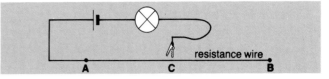

When the clip is attached to the resistance wire at **C** the bulb glows dimly.
a) Which way should the clip be moved to make the bulb glow more brightly?
b) Explain why this arrangement acts as a variable resistor.

4 A student makes a model of a house lighting circuit. The circuit he uses is shown below.

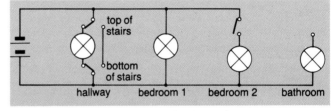

a) Which lamp will always be on?
b) Which lamp will never be on?
c) Explain why the light for the hallway cannot always be turned on and off by the switches at the top and bottom of the stairs.

5 The diagram below shows the plug connected to the flex of a metal table lamp.

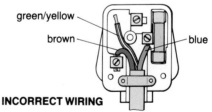

The wiring of this plug is dangerously wrong but the lamp still works.
a) Why does the lamp still work even though the live and neutral wires have been reversed?
b) Because the plug has been wired wrongly the switch is now connected to the neutral side of the supply. Explain why it would be dangerous to change the bulb in this lamp even with the switch turned off.

What are oscillations and waves?

How can we use them?

What is meant by frequency and wavelength?

What is the electromagnetic spectrum?

How does visible light behave?

Sound waves travel from musical instruments to our ears. Knowledge of the science of waves helps architects design concert halls with good acoustics. In some circumstances sound can be a nuisance and even cause damage.

Water waves arriving at a beach. Surfers may find large waves exciting but the constant pounding of waves erodes our coast. In other places the waves deposit sand and stones, building up the land.

This telescope receives radio waves sent out by very distant stars. Understanding them helps us to understand more about the history of the universe.

We use radio waves for communication. Radio and television programmes are transmitted by waves and received in our homes.

This oven uses microwaves to heat food rapidly.

Microwaves can also be used for communications. By using satellites in orbit around the Earth messages can be sent over large areas using microwaves.

Vibrations and the **waves** they cause play an important part in our everyday lives. We hear sound waves wherever we go. Some, like music, are pleasant, but others are irritating and dangerous. We also see light waves scattered from the objects around us. Our senses cannot detect radio waves but we can use them to send information, for example in the form of television programmes. We can feel the warmth produced by infra-red radiation and we can use microwaves to cook food.

The science of waves is well understood. The simple ideas in this chapter can be used to explain nearly all aspects of wave behaviour, from the very smallest waves due to vibrating atoms to the large water waves we see on our beaches.

Activities

1 Count and list the devices in your home which produce light waves.

2 Count and list the devices in your home which are designed to produce sound waves.

3 Count and list all the devices in your home which are designed to receive radio waves (including televisions).

4 Describe how your life would be different if radios and televisions did not exist.

Oscillations

A pendulum clock keeps good time because the pendulum moves backwards and forwards regularly. We call this type of movement an **oscillation**. Many mechanical systems oscillate if they are disturbed. For example, a child's swing will swing backwards and forwards if it is pushed once. Similarly a mass on a spring will bounce up and down if it is pulled down and then released. Because oscillations are regular they can be used for timing.

The time taken for one complete oscillation is called the **period**. Often we need to know how many oscillations are completed in one second. This is the **frequency** of the oscillation. For example, if a pendulum has a period of $^1/_2$s it will make two complete swings in 1 s. Its frequency is 2 cycles per second.

We can see that:

frequency = 1/period

Usually the frequency is written in units called **hertz** (Hz). 1 Hz = 1 cycle per second.

It is not only large things that oscillate. Even the atoms in a crystal vibrate. For example, a modern quartz watch keeps very good time because it contains a quartz crystal which vibrates regularly several thousand times every second.

Investigating oscillators

A simple pendulum can be made by hanging a bob on a length of string as shown in the diagram. When the bob is pulled to one side, it gains gravitational potential energy. When the bob is released this turns to kinetic energy as the bob starts to move. As it passes the centre (rest) position the bob starts to slow down and the energy changes back to potential energy . . .

During each oscillation the pendulum loses some energy due to friction, so the size or **amplitude** of the swing gets less until eventually it stops.

One oscillation is often too fast to time so we can use a stopwatch to time, say, 20 oscillations and then calculate the average time for one.

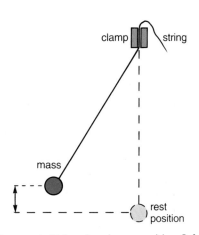

The mass is higher than its rest position. It has gravitational potential energy.

Activities

1 Set up a pendulum as shown and then investigate how its period depends on the length of the pendulum. Record your results in a table. (Don't forget to time complete oscillations.)

Measure the period for five different lengths. You will find that the period increases as the pendulum is made longer. Does doubling the length double the period? Can you find a pattern?

2 Using the same apparatus investigate whether changing the mass of the pendulum bob changes the time for one oscillation. (You will need to find a way of increasing the mass of the bob without changing the length of the pendulum.)

Questions

1 What is meant by
a) oscillation **b)** period
c) frequency?

2 A child on a swing goes backwards and forwards 100 times in five minutes. Calculate **a)** the period of the oscillation and **b)** the frequency in hertz.

3 The moon moves around the Earth once every 28 days (roughly). Work out the period of this 'oscillation' in seconds.

4 A pendulum clock is losing time.
   a) Is the period too long or too short?
   b) Should the pendulum be made shorter or longer?

More oscillators

There are many mechanical systems, other than pendulums, which oscillate. For example, the stretched string on a guitar oscillates when plucked. Springs are also good oscillators.

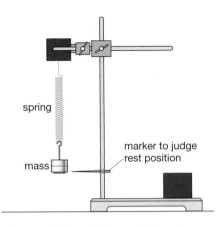

The diagram shows a mass on a spring resting at the equilibrium position. When the mass is pulled down, energy is stored in the stretched spring. When released the mass starts to move upwards, accelerated by the force of the spring. It shoots past the rest position and starts to compress the spring. The compressed spring gives a force downwards. This force slows the mass down until it just stops. Then the mass accelerates downwards past the rest position, and stretches the spring again. The motion keeps repeating itself. Like the pendulum, a mass oscillating on a spring keeps good time. During each oscillation the mass loses some of its energy to the air due to air resistance. The spring also heats up a bit as it is continually stretched and compressed.

Apparatus for investigating oscillations in a spring

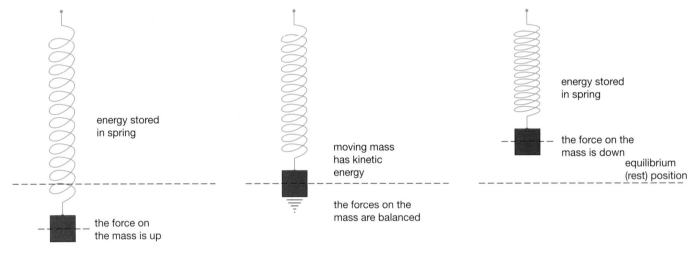

Activities

1 Set up a mass on a spring oscillator as shown above. Investigate how the period of oscillation changes as the mass is changed. Measure the period for at least five different masses. Can you find a relationship?

2 Set up a loaded beam oscillator as shown in the diagram. When the weighted end of the beam is pulled down and then released, the beam and the mass at the end oscillate. In fact it is the elasticity of the beam which provides the force in this oscillator. As you push the end of the beam down the top edge is stretched a bit and the surface underneath is compressed slightly.

Investigate how the period of oscillation changes as the length of the beam is altered. Measure the period for at least four different lengths. Can you find a relationship?

Investigate how the period varies with the mass taped to the end of the beam. Can you find a relationship?

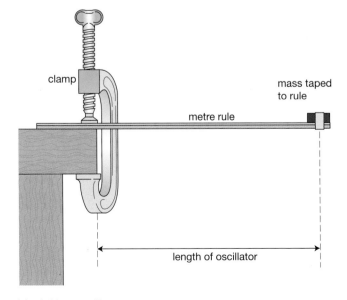

A loaded beam oscillator

Sound as a wave

Sound waves are caused by vibrations. Hitting a tuning fork or plucking a guitar string makes a musical note. The tuning fork's prongs oscillate backwards and forwards and the guitar's strings vibrate. In a television or radio the sound comes from a loudspeaker. Here the thin cone of the speaker vibrates backwards and forwards.

In all these cases the vibrations cause sound waves to move through the air to our ears where they are detected.

Sound can only move where there is a material. It cannot exist in a vacuum where there are no molecules to vibrate. The diagram shows apparatus to prove this. With air in the jar the sound from the loudspeaker can be heard quite clearly. As the air is pumped out the sound gets quieter. Eventually no sound can be heard. When the air is allowed to leak back in, the sound gets louder, proving that the loudspeaker was vibrating all the time.

Model of a sound wave

The cone of a loudspeaker moves backwards and forwards and sends a sound wave forwards in the air. The oscillation forces the air molecules closer together in some places (**compression**) and spreads them out in others (**rarefaction**). We can make a model of this by sending a wave down a long 'slinky' spring.

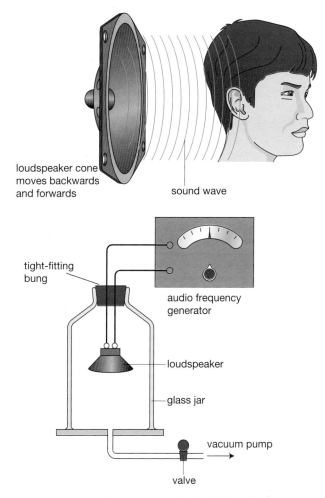

loudspeaker cone moves backwards and forwards

sound wave

tight-fitting bung

audio frequency generator

loudspeaker

glass jar

vacuum pump

valve

When the air is removed, no sound can be heard. Sound cannot travel in a vacuum.

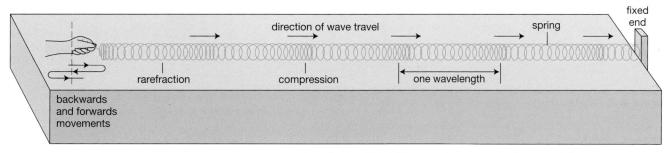

fixed end

direction of wave travel

spring

rarefraction

compression

one wavelength

backwards and forwards movements

The longitudinal wave on this spring has regions of compression and rarefaction. This is like a sound wave moving in a material.

The wave on the spring and sound waves are **longitudinal** waves. The oscillations causing them are in the same direction as the wave's motion.

Activities

1 Design and carry out simple experiments to prove that sound can travel through gases, solids, and liquids.

Danger! Noise!

Sound waves make the eardrum and the tiny bones inside the ear vibrate. Very loud sounds or prolonged exposure to noise can cause permanent damage.

People working with noisy machinery should wear ear defenders to protect their hearing.

Speed of sound

Sound waves take time to travel. A simple experiment can give an approximate value for the speed of sound in air. Two people stand 400 m apart in an open space. One has a starting pistol and the other has a stopwatch. When the gun is fired, the observer starts the watch immediately the smoke from the gun is seen. The watch is then stopped immediately the sound is heard. They do this three times and then change places and repeat the experiment in case the wind has been affecting the results. After three more timings an average time is calculated. The speed is given by:

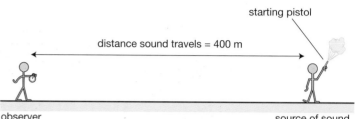

A simple experiment to measure the speed of sound

$$\text{speed of sound} = \frac{\text{distance between pistol and observer}}{\text{average time between smoke and sound}}$$

The speed of sound in air varies with temperature but is about 330 m/s at 0 °C. Sound travels at different speeds in different materials. In general it travels faster through liquids than gases and faster still through solids.

Questions

1 Science fiction films often show battles between spaceships. What would someone in space hear if an enemy spaceship exploded? Explain your answer.

2 A spectator at an athletics meeting is sitting about 200 m from the starter. She notices that the runners start off before she hears the starting pistol. Explain why.

3 At a swimming gala the time judges are at one end of the 33 m pool and the starter is at the other. They start their watches when they see the smoke from the starting pistol. Calculate what difference it would make if they waited to hear the sound before starting their watches.

4 In a thunderstorm the thunder is made at the same time as the lightning. Explain why an observer 1600 m away hears the thunder about 5 s after she sees the lightning. What time difference would there be if the storm was 2500 m away?

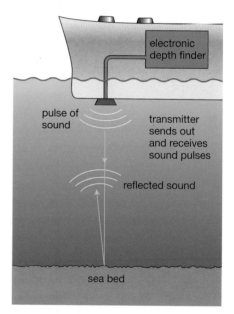

Finding distance using echoes

Ultrasound

The sound that we hear is a pressure wave in the air. Some pressure waves have a frequency too high for the human ear to detect. These are called **ultrasound**. They can be used at sea for finding depths or detecting shoals of fish. Because they can penetrate human tissue they can also be used to investigate inside the human body. The photograph shows an ultrasound source being used to study an embryo in the womb. The echoes from different substances and tissues are interpreted by the electronic equipment and shown on the monitor as a picture. This is a safe way of checking that the baby is developing normally.

Ultrasonic echoes allow the developing baby to be monitored safely.

Music and sound waves

Musical instruments make sound waves at frequencies which we find pleasing. These **notes** are then put together as music.

Stringed instruments produce notes by vibrating strings or wires. Percussion instruments are struck to make them vibrate.
Wind instruments produce notes when the air inside them vibrates.

frequency	notes
35 000 Hz	upper limit of hearing for dogs
20 000 Hz	upper limit of human hearing
10 000 Hz	shrill whistle
1 000 Hz	soprano singer
256 Hz	middle note on piano (middle C)
30 Hz	lowest note on piano

Frequency and pitch

A signal generator connected to a loudspeaker gives a musical note. By adjusting the frequency of the generator the frequency of the note can be changed. When the frequency is low the notes heard have a low pitch. When the frequency is increased the notes have a higher **pitch**.

A young person with normal hearing can hear notes from very low frequencies of about 10 Hz up to about 20 000 Hz. Older people may have a reduced hearing range. Some other animals can hear higher notes.

Waveforms

Musical notes can be displayed by connecting a microphone to a cathode ray oscilloscope. A pure musical note from a tuning fork or from a signal generator has a typical smooth wave shape. If the note is played more loudly the amplitude of the wave gets bigger but the number of waves per second (the frequency) stays the same.

Other instruments can give the same basic frequency as the tuning fork but have other frequencies or **overtones** added in. This makes the same note sound different on different instruments. The number and size of the overtones give the notes from different instruments a different **quality** or **timbre**.

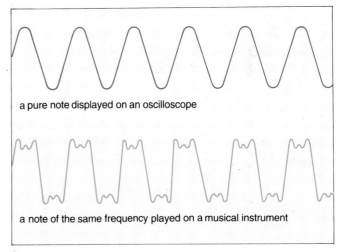

a pure note displayed on an oscilloscope

a note of the same frequency played on a musical instrument

*The overtones give the note from an instrument its complicated waveform and also its **quality** or **timbre**.*

Questions

1 List three instruments which make musical notes in each of the following ways: **a)** vibrating a string **b)** vibrating air in a tube **c)** vibrating a piece of metal or wood.

2 A violin for use in the school orchestra costs about £80. A Stradivarius violin (made by Stradivari, 1644–1737) plays the same notes but costs about £500 000. Suggest two reasons why a professional violinist would prefer to play a Stradivarius.

Vibrating strings

When a stretched string or wire is plucked it vibrates. Most of the vibrations die away very quickly but some continue for much longer. These are vibrations or waves which fit exactly on the string. At the lowest or **fundamental frequency** there are **nodes** at the fixed ends where the string cannot move. In the middle there is an **antinode** where the movement is greatest. You can see from the diagram that half a wavelength fits on the string. There are higher frequency waves which will also fit on the string. These are the overtones or harmonics which give the note its timbre. Some of these are shown in the diagram.

The apparatus shown opposite is called a **sonometer**. It can be used to investigate how the note produced by a stretched string or wire can be changed. By adding more weights the tension (force) in the string can be increased. The movable bridge can be used to lengthen or shorten the vibrating section. Thicker and thinner wires can also be used. The results of changing these things are shown below.

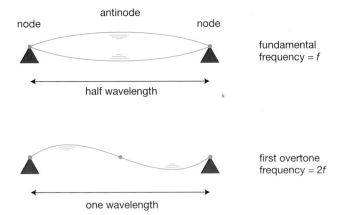

Vibrations on a string

change	result
use shorter wire	note is higher
use longer wire	note is lower
increase tension (force) in wire	note is higher
reduce tension in wire	note is lower
use thicker wire	note is lower

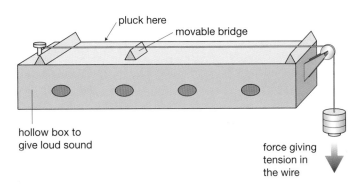

Investigating vibrations in a stretched wire

Activities

1 If you blow across the open top of a bottle you will hear a musical note. The note can be changed by pouring some water into the bottle and then blowing. (A note can also be produced by tapping the bottle with a spoon.) Investigate how the note changes as more water is added to the bottle. How do your findings compare with the result for a stretched wire?

Note that the bass (low pitch) strings on the guitar are thicker than the high pitch ones. The keys at the top allow the tension in the strings to be adjusted to tune the guitar. The guitarist can shorten the vibrating strings by pressing down with his/her fingers.

Electromagnetic waves

Waves on strings, water waves, and sound waves can only move through a material. However, there is a whole family of waves that can move in a vacuum as well as in materials. These are called the **electromagnetic waves**. They can be thought of as a magnetic wave and an electric wave moving together. They are produced when molecules, atoms, or even electrons vibrate when they are given extra energy.

There are several different types of electromagnetic wave. The type of wave depends on its frequency and wavelength, but all electromagnetic waves travel at the same speed. In a vacuum they all move at about 300 000 km/s! This is sometimes called the **speed of light** because the light we see is an electromagnetic wave.

The speed of light is so great that an electromagnetic wave can travel around the world seven times in one second! The diagram shows the complete range or **spectrum** of electromagnetic waves.

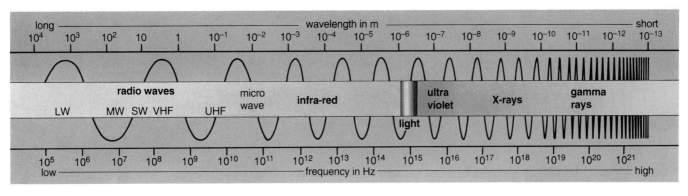

The electromagnetic spectrum

Visible light is a small part of the electromagnetic spectrum that can be detected by our eyes. We can see objects because they scatter (reflect) this light into our eyes.

The visible spectrum can be seen by passing white light through a glass prism. The different wavelengths are bent through slightly different angles. This is called dispersion. Different wavelengths are seen as different colours. When Sir Isaac Newton did this experiment he thought that he could detect seven different colours in the spectrum: red, orange, yellow, green, blue, indigo, and violet.

Visible light can be detected by the eye, photographic film, phototransistors, and light-dependent resistors.

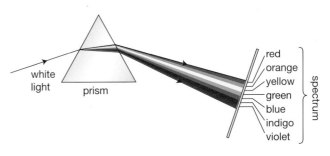

The dispersion of white light into a spectrum.

Questions

1 The moon is roughly 400 000 km away from the Earth. When astronauts first walked on the Moon they sent messages home by radio. How long did it take the radio waves to reach Earth?

2 The Sun is about 150 000 000 km from the Earth. How long does it take light from the Sun to reach us?

3 Alpha Centauri is a star which is about 4 light years from Earth. A light year is the distance travelled by light in one year. How far away is Alpha Centauri in kilometres?

The nature of light

We can only see something if light from it enters our eyes. **Luminous** objects give out their own light. Matches, candles, and fires emit light due to chemical reactions. Stars, like our Sun, give out light due to nuclear reactions. Fluorescent tubes and TV screens give out light when fast-moving electrons strike them.

Non-luminous objects do not emit light. We see them when they reflect light from a luminous source into our eyes. Note that stars are luminous, but planets and moons are not.

Our moon is not luminous. We only see the parts of it that reflect light from the Sun into our eyes.

Light rays and shadows

Light travels at very high speeds – up to 300 000 km/s in a vacuum! Light usually travels in straight lines. We can therefore represent beams of light by using a ruler to draw **rays**.

Rays of light pass through **transparent** objects but are blocked by **opaque** materials. So when an opaque object is placed in a beam of light, a shadow forms.

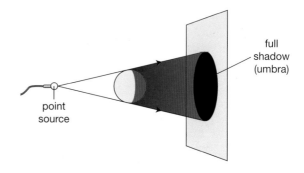

Small sources form sharp shadows.

If the light source is very small, a shadow with very sharp edges is seen. However, if the light source is large, the edges of the shadow are blurred. This is because in some places light from part, but not all, of the source can get through. This partial shadow is called the **penumbra**.

Lunar eclipses (see page 108) occur when the Moon blocks out light from the Sun.

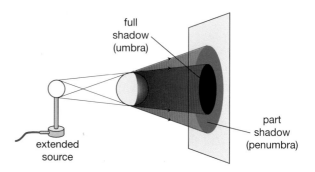

Larger sources give shadows with 'blurred' edges.

Questions

1 Light travels at about 300 000 km/s. Sound travels at about 300 m/s.
   a) How many times faster than sound is light?
   b) Why do you see a flash of lightning before you hear the thunder it causes?

2 When there is a full moon we can sometimes see things clearly, even at midnight. How is this possible?

3 Use this book to find information about lunar and solar eclipses.

4 **a)** Find out the dates of the lunar and solar eclipses that you may be able to see in the next six months.
   b) Why are lunar eclipses much more frequent than solar eclipses?

Reflection of light

Light travelling in air is **reflected** when it meets a different material. We see objects because they reflect light into our eyes. Rough surfaces reflect light at all angles in an irregular or **diffuse** way.

Law of reflection

When light meets a flat surface like a mirror, it is all reflected in the same way. The light rays are reflected at the same angle that they hit the mirror. The rule is:

angle of reflection = angle of incidence

Notice that we always measure the angles between the rays and the line at 90° to the mirror called the **normal**.

Images in mirrors

When light rays from an object strike a plane mirror, all the rays are reflected in this way. The result is that we see an image when we look back into the mirror. The image appears to be the same distance behind the mirror as the object is in front. This is a **virtual image** because no rays of light actually pass through it. The image in the mirror is **laterally inverted**. (It appears swapped from left to right.)

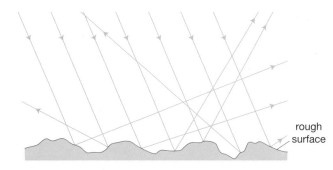

Diffuse reflection.

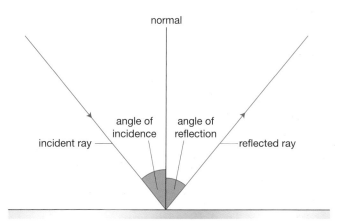

The angle of reflection is equal to the angle of incidence.

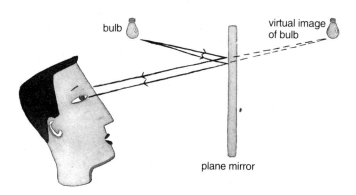

*The rays of light from the object (bulb) are reflected. The observer sees the image **behind** the mirror.*

Why are the words 'emergency ambulance' laterally inverted?

Questions

1 Draw an accurate diagram to show a ray of light hitting a mirror with an angle of incidence of 35°. Measure the angle between the two rays.

2 Explain, with examples, why some capital letters look the same in a mirror but others are 'reversed'.

3 A very small light bulb is placed 5 cm away from a plane mirror. Draw a full-size diagram showing the bulb and the mirror. Add two rays of light from the bulb to the mirror and then carefully draw in the reflected rays. Show where the image of the bulb is.

Refraction of light

Electromagnetic waves, including light, travel at about 300 000 km/s in air but they slow down when they enter any other material such as water or glass. If a ray of light meets the new material at an angle it bends. This is **refraction**.

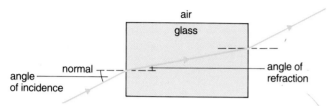

Refraction of light.

The diagram shows that light entering a glass block bends towards the normal. As it leaves the glass it speeds up again and so bends away from the normal. The ray emerging from this rectangular block is parallel to the ray going in. Rays of different colours are bent through slightly different angles. In a prism this disperses the colours, spreading them out into a spectrum.

Refraction in different materials

When light enters a material at an angle, it changes direction because its speed changes. If the material is very dense, the light slows down more and so the angle of refraction is larger. The diagrams compare light entering glass and diamond at an angle of 60°.

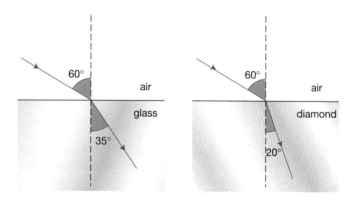

The **refractive index** of a material tells us how much refraction occurs. The table opposite shows the values for some transparent materials. It is the high refractive index of diamonds that causes them to sparkle.

Apparent depth

One of the effects of refraction is that our brains can be tricked into thinking that pools of water are shallower or glass blocks are thinner than they really are. The **apparent depth** is given by the real depth divided by the refractive index. The refractive index of water is about ⁴⁄₃ so a 2 m pool looks 1.5 m deep.

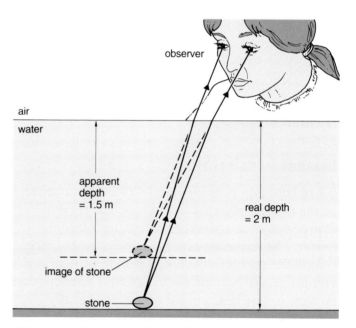

Refraction makes the water look shallower.

Table of refractive indices

material	refractive index
air	1.00
water	1.33
Perspex	1.49
window glass	1.51
flint ('lens') glass	1.61
diamond	2.40

Refraction and the critical angle

In the diagrams below you can see what happens when the angle of incidence inside a glass block increases from 35° to 50°. At 35° most of the light gets out of the glass with just a small part being reflected. At about 42° the refracted ray just gets out of the block but much more of the light is being reflected. This is the **critical angle**. At angles greater than 42° all the light is reflected. This is called **total internal reflection**.

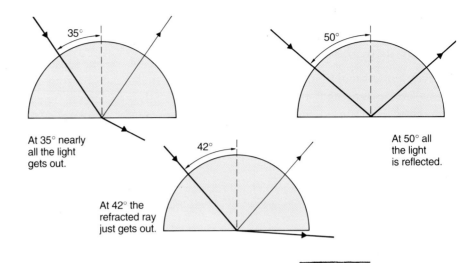

At 35° nearly all the light gets out.

At 42° the refracted ray just gets out.

At 50° all the light is reflected.

Using total internal reflection

Many optical instruments use total internal reflection inside prisms. The image is just like that formed by mirrors but there is no need for a reflective coating which can corrode.

Optical fibres

An **optical fibre** is a thin fibre of glass which light can pass down. The diagram shows that the light always hits the side of the fibre at an angle greater than the critical angle. All the light is reflected and so little energy is lost. The light emerges from the other end of the fibre almost as bright as it went in. The fibres are very thin so they can be bundled together and used as a **light pipe**.

Light pipes can be used for inspection inside machinery or even inside the human body. The outside fibres carry light down to illuminate the object. Light reflected from the object then travels up the middle fibres to a special camera or eyepiece.

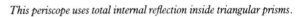

glass prism — light

observer

This periscope uses total internal reflection inside triangular prisms.

Optical fibres can also carry coded signals as pulses of light from a laser. These can then be changed into electrical signals at the receiving end. For example many of our telephone calls are now transmitted down light pipes which can carry several thousand conversations at once! Glass fibres are more efficient at transmitting messages than copper wires and so fewer booster stations are needed. This keeps costs low.

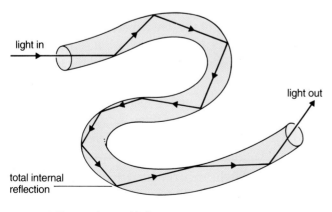

light in

light out

total internal reflection

An optical fibre greatly magnified

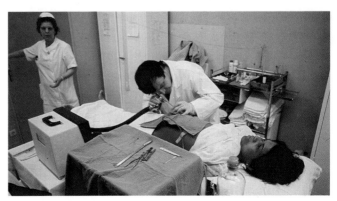

Fibre optics allow surgeons to watch as they manipulate instruments inside the body.

Refraction in lenses

Lenses are pieces of glass shaped to have a focusing effect. They come in a huge variety of shapes and sizes but there are two basic shapes: **convex** and **concave**.

Convex lenses bend light towards a central axis so they are called **converging lenses**. Concave lenses bend the light away from the axis so are called **diverging lenses**.

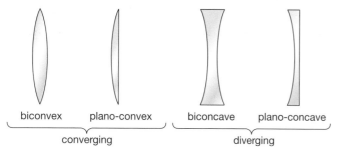

Lens shapes

The diagram shows how parallel light rays passing through a converging lens are brought together at a **focal point**. Parallel rays passing through a diverging lens are bent as if they came from a single focal point. The distance between the centre of a lens and its focal point is called the **focal length**. Powerful lenses have short focal lengths; weak lenses have long focal lengths.

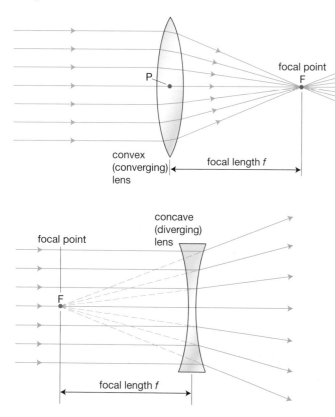

Action of a concave lens

Finding the approximate focal length of a lens

The focal length of a lens can be found by focusing light from a very distant object such as the Sun on to a screen. The distance between the centre of the lens and the screen (the focal length) is then measured.

In the laboratory it is easier to focus light from the windows on the other side of the room on to a wall or screen. The windows will be about three or four metres away so we can think of them as being fairly distant objects. When the image is sharply focused the distance between the centre of the lens and the screen can be measured. This gives a good approximation to the focal length of the lens.

When you do this experiment notice that the image is small, and upside down.

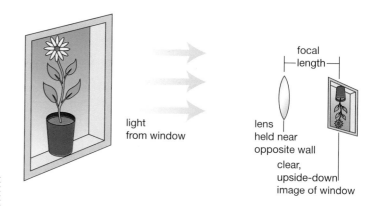

Finding the approximate focal length of a lens

Questions

1 Describe in words the shape of **a)** a concave lens **b)** a plano-convex lens.

2 After a practical lesson, a teacher finds that the students have not put the lenses back in the right packets. The lenses are all biconvex but some have focal lengths of 10 cm, others 20 cm, and the rest 25 cm.

  a) How can she quickly sort the powerful 10 cm lenses from the weaker 20 cm and 25 cm lenses?
  b) She can't see any obvious difference between the remaining lenses. How can she sort them out?

3 Explain why the experiment to measure focal length described on this page works for converging lenses but not diverging lenses.

Images formed by converging lenses

The position and size of the image formed by a convex lens depends on how far the object is from the lens. If the object is further away than the focal length of the lens then the image is **real**. This is because the lens can bring the light rays to a focus. If the object is so close that it is inside the focal length of the lens then the image is **virtual**. It cannot be seen on a screen. You see it by looking back into the lens.

We can draw ray diagrams to find what the image will be like. Usually two or three rays are drawn using these rules:

- **Any ray through the optical centre of the lens passes straight through without being bent.**
- **Any ray parallel to the axis of the lens passes through the focal point after it leaves the lens.**
- **Any ray through the focal point of the lens leaves parallel to the axis of the lens.**

Convex lens forming a small, real image of the Sun

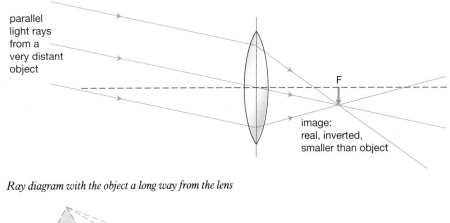

Ray diagram with the object a long way from the lens

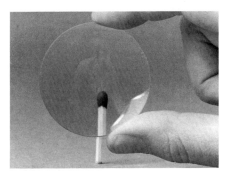

With the object close to the lens the image is magnified.

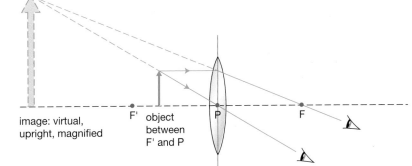

Ray diagram with the object less than one focal length from the lens

Images in concave lenses

The image formed by a concave lens is always virtual, upright, and smaller than the object.

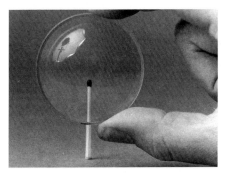

The image formed by a concave lens is smaller than the object and upright.

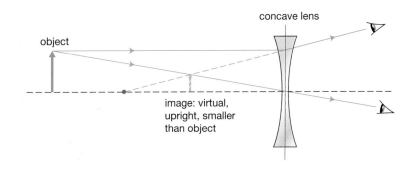

Ray diagram for an object viewed through a concave lens

Using lenses

One of the oldest and certainly the most common use of lenses is to improve the vision of people with poor eyesight. The lenses may be made of glass or plastic. They can be large lenses in spectacles or very small contact lenses worn in the eye.

Short-sighted people can see things clearly which are close but they cannot focus on things which are far away. For example they may see the print in a book but be unable to read a distant road sign. This is because the lens in the eye is too powerful or because the eyeball is too short.

Long-sighted people can see distant things clearly but cannot focus on things close to them. This may be because the lens in the eye is too weak. Old people tend to be long-sighted.

Opticians can provide lenses to focus the light from an object on the retina of the eye so that the person can see clearly. Short-sighted people need concave lenses and long-sighted people need convex lenses.

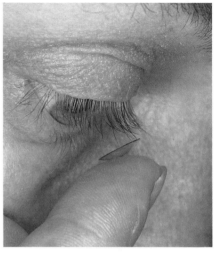

A contact lens is a thin, plastic lens which is placed on the cornea of the eye.

The camera

A **camera** has a convex lens at the front to focus light on to the film loaded into the camera. The image formed is real, smaller than the object, and upside down.

Behind the lens there is a shutter which is usually closed. This keeps all the light from the film. When the camera button is pressed the shutter opens for a short period of time (usually less than 0.01 second). This exposes the film. This image is recorded by chemicals in the film. The film is then developed and printed on special paper.

*A modern **single lens reflex** camera*

Cheap cameras have a lens fixed so that it is one focal length from the film. In photographs taken with these cameras things far away appear sharply in focus but things close to the camera are out of focus and blurred. The camera shown has a lens which can be moved backwards and forwards. This allows things which are far away *and* those close by to be brought into focus.

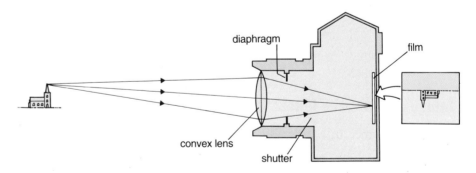

Ray diagram for a camera taking a photograph of a distant object

Activities

1 Cheap cameras have fixed lenses and so only distant things are in focus.
Design an experiment to find out how close the camera can be to the object before the photograph is blurred. If you have or can borrow a cheap camera carry out the experiment but remember that film and developing are expensive. (*Hint:* you could get away with taking just one photograph.)

2 If you have or can borrow a camera of the single lens reflex (SLR) type, design and carry out an experiment to find the effect of changing **a)** the shutter speed **b)** the size of the aperture. (*Note:* a camera with automatic controls only is not suitable for this activity.)

Coloured light

Our eyes can only detect electromagnetic waves with a small range of frequencies. However, we have already seen that white light can be split up into a range of colours called the visible spectrum. In fact our eyes contain just three types of colour sensors. One type responds to red light, another to green light, and the third to blue light. Red, blue, and green are called the **primary colours**. If our eyes receive red, blue, and green light together we 'see' white light. This can be shown by shining three coloured spotlights on to a screen so that they overlap. Where the three primary colours combine we see white light. Where only two primary colours add we see **secondary colours**. The following table shows the rules of colour addition for light.

primary colours	colour 'seen' by eye
red + green + blue	white
red + green	yellow
red + blue	magenta
green + blue	cyan (peacock blue)

By varying the amounts of each primary colour present you can see any colour of the spectrum. This is used in the colour television.

In a black and white (monochrome) television there is an electron gun rather like the one in a cathode ray oscilloscope. The beam of electrons is moved quickly across the screen and more slowly downwards. This gives parallel lines all over the screen. The picture is produced by varying the brightness of the spot as it moves. About 25 new pictures are produced every second so our eyes see a smoothly moving picture.

Television screens are coated with **phosphors**. These are chemicals which give out light when hit by the beam of electrons. In a colour television the screen is coated with thousands of small phosphor strips in groups of three – one which gives red light, one which gives green, and one which gives blue. The television has three separate electron guns, one for each colour. The colour seen on the screen depends on which phosphors are being struck by electrons. For example, when the red and green strips glow we see yellow.

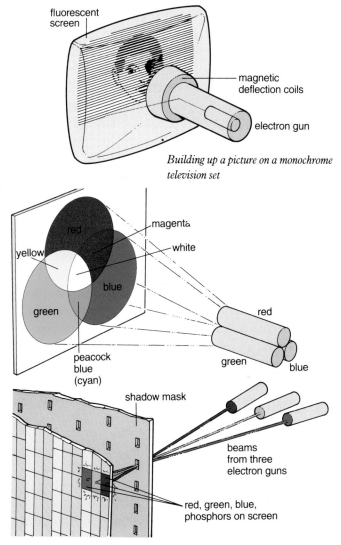

Building up a picture on a monochrome television set

A colour television uses three electron guns

Questions

1 Name the colours of the visible spectrum. Which one has the longest wavelength?

2 Name the three primary colours for light. What colours do we get by adding the following coloured lights together:
   a) red + green **b)** blue + green **c)** cyan + red **d)** yellow + blue?

3 Explain why a colour television is more expensive than a monochrome (black and white) one.

4 Why are only three phosphors needed on a colour television screen?

5 What colours do you see on a television screen when the following phosphors glow:
   a) red + blue **b)** blue + green **c)** red + blue + green?

Looking at coloured objects

White light from the Sun or from a light bulb contains all the colours of the spectrum. Why do many objects look coloured? The answer is that the materials they are made of absorb some of the colours of the spectrum and reflect the rest. As a result we only see the colours of the reflected light. The diagram shows what happens when we look at a red rose in white light. We call chemicals which reflect only certain colours pigments. Paints, inks, and coloured crayons contain pigments. So do the petals and leaves of plants and the skins of animals. Some mixtures of pigments will absorb all the colours of the spectrum. These appear black.

Mixing pigments

There are three **primary pigment colours**: red, blue, and yellow. With them a wide range of other colours can be made. This is because the pigments do not reflect just one colour but a small part of the spectrum. For example, blue paint absorbs red, orange, and yellow light but reflects blue, green, and violet light. The diagram shows how green light is reflected from a mixture of blue and yellow pigments.

Filters

A filter is a coloured piece of glass or plastic which lets through some colours but filters out all the others. For example, a red filter lets red light through but absorbs green and blue light. Looking through coloured filters or shining coloured light on objects may make them look different colours.

A green apple looks green because it reflects green light. If we now look at it in red light it looks black. This is because there is no green light to reflect!

Questions

1 **a)** Why does a daffodil's flower look yellow and its leaves look green?
   b) What colour would a daffodil plant look through a red filter?

2 A set of snooker balls includes red, blue, green, yellow, black, and white balls. Explain why it would be difficult to play snooker under a blue light.

3 **a)** Write down the rules for mixing red, blue, and green light.
   b) Write down the rules for mixing red, blue, and yellow pigments (paint).

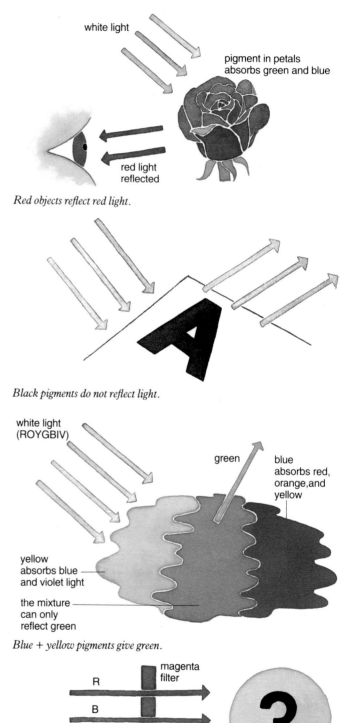

Red objects reflect red light.

Black pigments do not reflect light.

Blue + yellow pigments give green.

This yellow ball would look red under magenta light.

4 An actor wears a peacock blue (cyan) jacket. What colour does it look to the audience when he is lit by a spotlight covered by **a)** a green filter **b)** a red filter **c)** a magenta filter?

1 A pendulum is an oscillator.
a) What is an oscillation?
b) What is meant by i) the period   ii) the frequency of an oscillation?
c) Describe how you would measure the period of a simple pendulum 30 cm long.
d) What would happen to i) the period ii) the frequency if the pendulum was made shorter?

2 The diagram shows the side view of a water wave.

a) Copy the diagram and mark on the wavelength and the amplitude of the wave.
b) The wave shown is moving at 2.5 m/s and has a wavelength of 15 m. What is the frequency of the wave?

3 All waves can transfer energy.
a) Explain how energy can be transferred from a loudspeaker to your ear.
b) Explain how energy from the Sun is transferred to the Earth.
c) There is obviously lots of chemical activity on the Sun. Why can't we hear any noise from the Sun?

4 **a)** What is an echo?
b) Some fishermen use echoes to locate shoals of fish beneath their boats. Suggest how this works.
c) A mountaineer shouts for help. Half a second later (0.5 s) she hears the echo. How far away is the rock face which is reflecting her voice?
(Take the speed of sound to be 330 m/s.)

5 A microphone is connected to a cathode ray oscilloscope. A tuning fork giving a pure musical note of frequency 256 Hz (middle C) is held in front of the microphone. The trace produced on the screen is shown below.

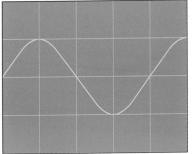

Draw to the same scale the traces you would expect to see if
a) the tuning fork was held closer to the microphone so that the note was louder
b) a tuning fork of lower pitch was held in front of the microphone
c) the microphone was placed near to a piano and the note middle C played. Explain why this diagram is not the same as the one given in the question.

6 The main regions of the electromagnetic spectrum are given below.

radio waves   visible light   gamma rays
microwaves   ultraviolet light   infra-red
X-rays

a) State two things that all these waves have in common.
b) Compare the wavelengths and frequencies of radio waves and X-rays.
c) What do the letters UV stand for?
d) Give two uses for microwaves.
e) Give one use for X-rays.
f) What colours make up the visible spectrum? radio waves.

7 The diagram below shows an object 4 cm high at a distance of 9 cm from a convex lens of focal length 6 cm. The diagram is not to scale.

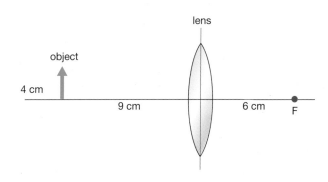

Draw the diagram to a scale of 1 cm representing 2 cm (i.e. half real size). Make sure that the object is on the left-hand edge of your page.

Draw two rays from the top of the image through the lens to find the position of the image.

Is the image real or virtual?

How large is the image?

7 Magnetism and electricity

What is magnetism?
What is electromagnetism?
How can we use magnetism in technology?
What effect have electronic devices had on our lives?
How can information be stored digitally?

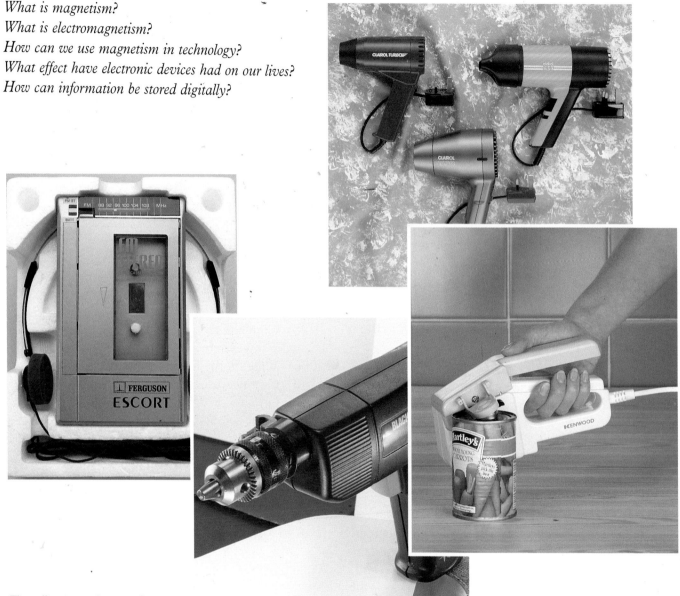

These all use magnetism to work.

Magnetism is a mysterious force which appears between magnets, and between magnets and materials like iron and steel. For example, a magnet will attract steel needles placed close to it.

A piece of steel or other alloy which has been magnetized so that it keeps its magnetic properties is called a **permanent magnet**. An electric current also exerts a magnetic force. We can use this fact to make magnets which can be turned on and off. These are **electromagnets**.

Magnetic forces act over relatively small distances, usually just a few centimetres, but we can use them to great effect. All the devices shown on this page use

magnetism. The can opener uses a permanent magnet to hold the lid, the motor of the electric drill uses electromagnets, and the headphones use both!

Activities

1 Make a list of all the devices in your home that use magnetism. Look for magnetic door catches, appliances with motors, loudspeakers, etc.

2 Design an experiment to test the statement **magnetic forces only act over small distances**. Draw the apparatus you would use and describe how you would carry out the investigation.

Magnetic effects: attraction and repulsion

A permanent magnet is very useful for picking up steel dressmakers' pins or steel nails, but it has no effect on copper wire or brass screws. In fact, there are only three elements which are strongly attracted to magnets: iron, nickel, and cobalt. Magnets also attract alloys which contain iron, nickel, or cobalt, for example steel.

Our planet also affects magnets. As a result, a bar magnet which is hung from a thread as shown in the diagram eventually settles down to point roughly north to south. The end of the magnet which points to the north is called the north-seeking pole. The other end is the south-seeking pole. We usually call these the north and south poles of the magnet, or just 'N' and 'S'.

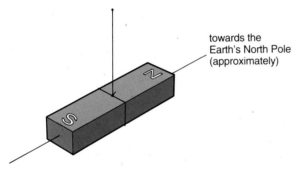

towards the Earth's North Pole (approximately)

A magnet acting as a compass.

experiment	result
N pole brought near to S pole	attracts
S pole brought near to N pole	attracts
N pole brought near to N pole	repels
S pole brought near to S pole	repels
Like poles repel, unlike poles attract	

Questions

1 You have a bar magnet but the N and S poles are not marked. Describe briefly how you could find which end was south seeking.

2 A bar magnet is suspended from a piece of thin thread. What would happen if the following were brought near:

    a) an unmagnetized iron rod

    b) a copper rod

    c) the S pole of another magnet?

3 Some books say that 'repulsion is the only test for a magnet'. Why is attraction on its own is not enough.

Magnetic fields

When you bring a magnet close to a steel pin, the pin starts to move before the magnet touches it. The pin may even jump across a small gap to stick to the magnet. This is because there is a space around the magnet where magnetic materials 'feel' a force. We say that there is a **magnetic field** around the magnet.

Magnetic fields can be studied using iron filings and small compasses called plotting compasses. When iron filings are sprinkled on to a piece of card covering a bar magnet, each filing becomes magnetized and lines up with the magnetic field. This gives a pattern which tells us about the shape of the field. In fact, the field is all around the magnet in three dimensions. We can show this by dipping a magnet into iron filings.

The direction of magnetic field lines can be found using a plotting compass. The compass needle is a small magnet which can turn on a pivot. In a magnetic field its N pole is pulled one way and its S pole is pulled the other. The needle comes to rest in line with the magnetic field.

A typical field pattern for a bar magnet is shown in the diagram. Only a few lines are drawn to show the shape clearly. The spacing of the lines shows the strength of the field. Where the lines are close together, for example near the poles, the field is strong. A large force would act on a magnetic pole placed there.

The arrows on the field lines show the direction of the force which would act on a N pole. This is always from the N of the magnet to the S.

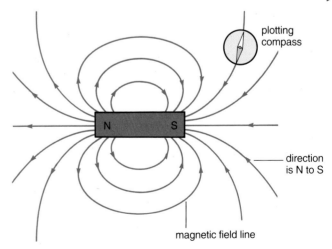

plotting compass

direction is N to S

magnetic field line

Magnetic field pattern for a bar magnet. Notice that the field is strongest near the poles.

Experiments show us the basic properties of magnets and magnetic materials but they don't help to explain what is happening. We need a theory to explain the effects of magnetism and to help us use it in technology.

Evidence for the theory

A magnetized steel rod has a N pole at one end and a S pole at the other. It can be snapped in two. When each piece is tested it is found to be a complete magnet; each piece has its own N and S poles. If we keep breaking them into smaller and smaller pieces we get smaller and smaller complete magnets. We never get a N pole on its own, or a free S pole!

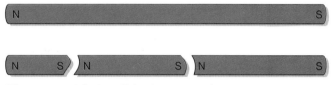

*When a magnet is broken **all** the pieces are complete magnets.*

We can think of magnetic materials as containing 'magnets' within their molecules. (These tiny 'molecular magnets' are actually due to the movement of electrons around atoms.)

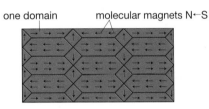

Unmagnetized iron

Inside a material like iron the molecular magnets can line up in groups called **domains**. The diagram shows how the domains are arranged in a piece of unmagnetized iron. Notice that the molecular magnets inside each domain are lined up, but that different domains line up in other directions. They seem to form loops which cancel each other out. This leaves the iron **unmagnetized**.

Now when the iron is placed near to a magnet, its molecular magnets start to line up. The domains in one particular direction start to grow. In the diagram of a magnetized piece of iron you can see that all the large domains point in the same direction. This leaves free poles at the ends. In the middle the N and S poles of the molecular magnets cancel out.

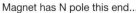

Magnetized iron

Using the theory

A piece of iron can be magnetized by stroking it repeatedly with a magnet.

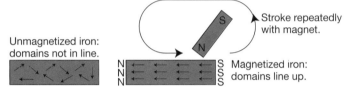

The N pole of the stroking magnet attracts the S poles of the 'molecular magnets' as it moves across the iron.

A permanent magnet can be demagnetized by heating it up and then quickly cooling it in cold water. The diagrams show what happens to the domains when this is done.

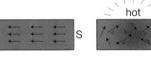

Magnet with domains aligned.

Energy from heating causes molecules to move faster and domains to become unaligned.

Taking away energy quickly leaves the domains 'frozen' in a random pattern.

Demagnetizing by heating and rapid cooling

Questions

1 A carpenter finds that her screwdriver has become magnetized. She demagnetizes it by hitting it several times with a hammer.
   a) Using the domain theory, explain why this method works.
   b) Explain why science teachers get annoyed when students drop magnets on the floor.

2 If a piece of steel is heated and then allowed to cool slowly it becomes a magnet. Explain this using the idea of molecular magnets.

Magnetic induction

When a piece of iron or steel is placed near to a magnet the magnetic domains line up and it becomes magnetized. We say that the magnet has **induced** magnetism in the metal. You can see from the diagrams that the induced pole closest to the magnet's N pole is a S pole. This explains why magnets attract iron and steel.

When the iron is pulled away from the magnet it loses its induced magnetism. It was a **temporary** magnet. However when steel is used it keeps some of the induced magnetism and becomes a **permanent** magnet.

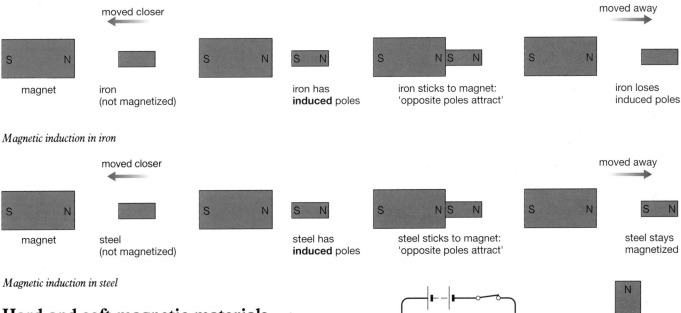

Magnetic induction in iron

Magnetic induction in steel

Hard and soft magnetic materials

Iron is referred to as a **soft** magnetic material. It is easy to magnetize but it loses its magnetism easily. This makes it useful where a temporary magnet is needed or where the direction of the magnetism has to be changed quickly. Electromagnets, electric motors, and transformers all use iron. Steel and similar alloys are **hard** magnetic materials. They are more difficult to magnetize than iron but do not lose their magnetism easily. They make good permanent magnets. They are also used in recording tapes and computer diskettes for storing information.

Making a permanent magnet

You saw on the opposite page how a piece of steel can be magnetized by stroking it with a magnet. The magnet is moved over the steel many times, always in the same direction. Gradually the steel develops strong, induced poles. A better way of making a permanent magnet is to place the steel inside a coil of wire. When an electric current flows in the coil, strong magnetic poles are induced in the steel.

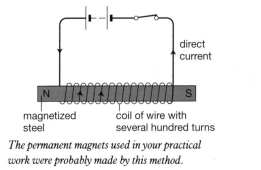

The permanent magnets used in your practical work were probably made by this method.

Activities

1 The diagram shows a magnet attracting some steel pins. See how many steel pins or paperclips a strong magnet will support.

a) Explain how this happens using the idea of induced poles.

b) Use a plotting compass to test whether your pins or paperclips have been left magnetized by the experiment.

c) Explain how you could use the situation shown in the diagram to compare the strengths of two magnets.

d) Can you think of any other way of comparing the strengths of two magnets?

Electric currents and magnetism

In 1820 a Danish scientist called Oersted showed that if a compass was placed below a wire carrying an electric current, the compass needle moved. He had shown that a wire carrying an electric current has a magnetic field around it. We call this effect **electromagnetism**. The discovery of the connection between electric currents and magnetism was very important. Much of our modern technology depends on it.

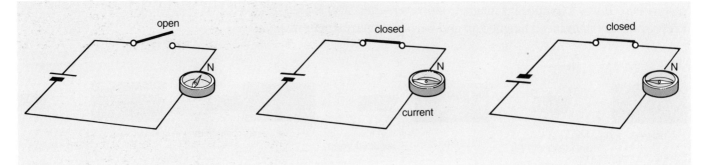

No current: compass lines up with Earth's field   *With current: compass needle deflected*   *With current reversed: compass needle deflected in opposite direction*

Experiments with iron filings and plotting compasses give the following results:

- The magnetic field lines are circles around the wire.
- The direction of the field (i.e. how a free N pole would move) is clockwise if we look in the direction of conventional current flow (+ to −).
- If the current is reversed then the magnetic field also reverses.
- If the size of the current is increased then the magnetic field gets stronger.
- The field is strongest close to the wire and gets much weaker as you move further away.

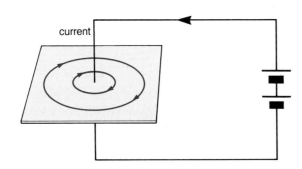

The current in the wire gives a circular magnetic field.

Magnetic fields and coils

When a current flows in a long coil with many loops of wire the magnetic field looks just like that of a bar magnet. A coil like this is called a **solenoid**.

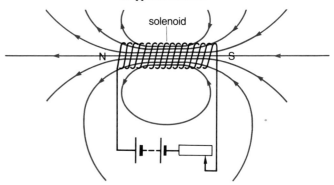

The field pattern of a solenoid is like that of a bar magnet.

The direction of the field in a solenoid can be found by using the fingers of your right hand to show the direction of the current in the loops of wire. Your right thumb then shows the N pole of the solenoid.

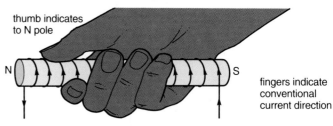

*This **right-hand grip rule** can be used to predict where the N pole of a solenoid will be.*

In a solenoid the field can be made stronger by:

- increasing the current
- making more loops of wire (in the same length)
- putting a core of iron or steel inside the coil (this makes the field much stronger).

Electromagnets are used for lifting scrap iron and steel. The magnet has a coil of copper wire wound around an iron core. The iron becomes strongly magnetized when a current flows in the coil. The core then loses its magnetism when the current is turned off. Iron is a soft magnetic material.

Electromagnets can also be used to separate ferrous metals like iron and steel from non-ferrous metals like copper and aluminium. They are also used in many other devices such as relays, loudspeakers, and motors.

Electromagnet lifting 'ferrous' scrap

Questions

1 The diagram shows the magnetic field pattern around a current in a wire. Copy the diagram, then draw (to the same scale) diagrams to show what happens when **a**) the current is increased **b**) the current is reversed.

wire carrying current into page

2 Look up the chemical symbol for iron. Suggest why scrap dealers call old car bodies 'ferrous scrap'.

3 Food cans are often made of steel plated with tin. Drinks cans are usually made of aluminium. Explain how a metal recycling plant could use an electromagnet. Explain why metal recycling is important.

4 Explain using the domain theory why the iron core inside a solenoid becomes magnetized.

A reed relay can be operated by a small bar magnet (shown) or an electromagnet.

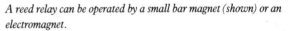

no magnet: switch open

magnet nearby: switch closed

electromagnet on: switch closed

Relays

A **relay** is an electrically controlled switch. It uses a small current to turn on a separate circuit, which may carry a large current. The diagram shows a relay to turn on the starter motor of a car. On starting, a very large current flows through the motor circuit. If it flowed through the wires to the ignition switch it would melt them!

In electronic circuits, small reed relays are used. These have a very thin, flexible piece of metal inside a glass tube. The metal acts as a switch. When a magnet is nearby, the switch becomes magnetized and the contacts touch. The relay can be activated by a small bar magnet or a small coil. Some reed relays have their contacts together under normal conditions. The switch then **opens** in a magnetic field.

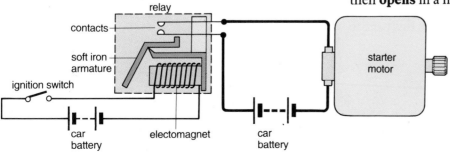

relay

contacts

soft iron armature

ignition switch

car battery

electomagnet

car battery

starter motor

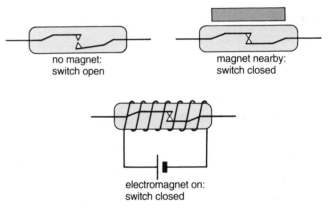

*When the ignition switch is closed a **small** current flows in the electromagnet. The iron armature is attracted to the electromagnet, closing the relay contacts. A **large** current flows in the starter circuit as the motor turns the engine.*

Magnetism, currents, and forces

The diagram shows an experiment to demonstrate the effect of a magnetic field on a current-carrying wire. A short piece of wire, W, rests on wires which make up the rest of the circuit. When the switch is closed a current flows in the direction shown. The wire W moves off to the right showing that there is a force in that direction. Notice that the wire is **not** attracted by the poles of the magnet.

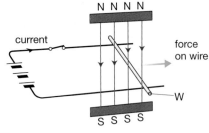

The motor effect

The experiment can be repeated with the magnetic field reversed. This time the wire moves in the opposite direction, i.e. to the left.

If the magnetic field is left as it is in the diagram but the current is made to flow in the opposite direction, the wire moves off to the left.

Reversing the magnetic field changes the direction of the force.
Reversing the current in the wire also reverses the direction of the force.

We can draw a diagram to show the relative directions of the current, magnetic field, and force which makes the wire move. Notice that the force is at right angles to both the current and the magnetic field.

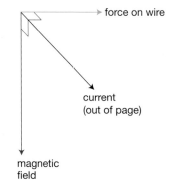

In the motor effect, the force is at right angles to the magnetic field and current.

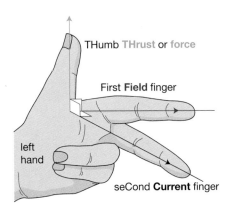

*Fleming's **left-hand motor rule** uses the first two fingers and the thumb of the left hand to show how the directions of the force, field, and current are linked.*

Questions

1 Copy the diagram on this page which shows the directions of the current, magnetic field, and force on the wire. Mark the arrows C, M, and F.

   a) Draw a similar diagram to show what happens to the direction of the force when the current is reversed

   b) Draw a third diagram to show what would happen if the current and the magnetic field were reversed.

2 The rule for finding the direction of the force is sometimes called **Fleming's left-hand motor rule**. Show that it only works with the left hand and that the right hand gives the wrong answer.

3 The diagram shows a loop of wire in a circuit. The wire passes between the poles of a magnet. Use the diagrams on this page to work out what will happen to the wire in the magnetic field.

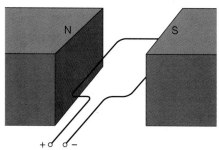

Electric motors

When an electric current flows in a wire in a magnetic field, a force is produced. The force can make the wire move. This is sometimes called the **motor effect**. Scientists and engineers have used this effect to build the electrical motors which are so important in our modern lifestyles. These range from the small motors which move the tape in cassette players to the powerful motors which move the trains on the electrified parts of our railway system.

In the diagram, a single loop of wire carries a current in the direction shown. The piece of wire on the left feels a force upwards, but the piece on the right feels a force downwards. These opposite forces make the loop of wire start to turn. This twisting effect is used in electric motors.

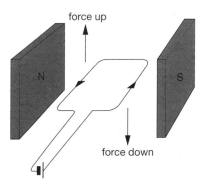

The two forces on this coil are making it twist.

Simple d.c. motors

In a real motor, we want the coil to keep spinning in the same direction. We do this by controlling the current direction. The diagram shows how this is done in a simple motor designed to work from a battery or other direct current (d.c.) supply The motor has a rectangular coil of wire between N and S poles of a magnet. The coil can spin on an axle. The coil is connected to two halves of a copper ring which has been cut through. The split ring is called the **commutator**. The battery is connected to the coil through two carbon blocks which rub against the commutator. (The carbon blocks are called **brushes** because early electric motors used brushes of metal wire to make the contacts.)

The commutator spins with the coil and makes sure that the current always flows in the right direction to keep the motor spinning.

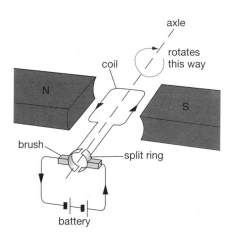

Simple d.c. motor

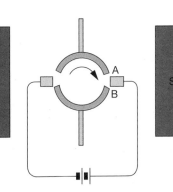

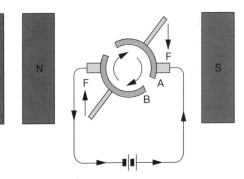

When the coil is flat, the forces on its sides are opposite, so the coil turns.

In this position there is no turning effect but the inertia of the coil keeps it turning.

As the coil passes the top, each brush connects with the other half of the split ring. This keeps the current flowing in the right direction.

Activities

1 List all the appliances in your home which use electric motors. For each appliance state whether the motor uses d.c. or a.c. current. (Think carefully about portable cassette players which can use batteries or mains!)

2 List all the devices in a car which use an electric motor. (Your answer will depend on the type of car you choose, but all cars have at least two.)

3 If you can, take the top off a motorized toy. Look for the motor and then identify the coil, the magnets, the commutator, and the brushes.

The motor effect again!

Another common application of the motor effect is in the **loudspeaker**. Cassette players, radios, and stereo systems usually use moving-coil loudspeakers.

The photograph shows a moving-coil loudspeaker and the diagram underneath it shows its parts. It has a permanent magnet shaped like a cylinder. This gives a strong magnetic field in the circular gap between the poles. A coil of wire rests in the gap. One end of the coil is fixed to a paper or plastic cone. Thin wires lead from the coil to connectors at the back of the loudspeaker cabinet. These are connected to a current supply. This can be an amplifier circuit inside a radio, television, cassette player, or even an electronic musical instrument. The output from the current supply will be an alternating current which has a frequency in the audible range (10 Hz to 20 kHz).

When an alternating current flows in the coil, the coil moves backwards and forwards making the cone vibrate at the same frequency as the current. The cone makes the air in front of it vibrate and move away as a wave. We hear this as sound.

If the volume is turned up, the size of the current is increased. This gives a bigger force on the coil and so the cone moves further. This in turn pushes the air molecules in front further. The result is a louder sound. If the current from the amplifier has a high frequency, the coil, and therefore the cone, moves backwards and forwards many times per second. This gives a high pitched sound.

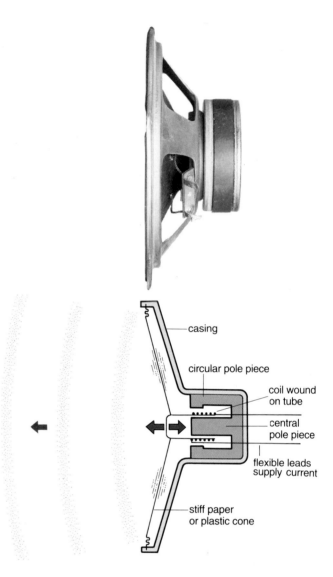

The photograph and diagram show a moving-coil loudspeaker. If you can, look at a real loudspeaker. Look for the magnet, the contacts for the coil, and the cone.

Questions

1 Give two ways in which a loudspeaker is like a motor. Give two differences between a loudspeaker and a motor.

2 Good loudspeakers have their paper cones attached to a heavy metal frame. Suggest why this is.

3 A student fixes a pair of loudspeakers into special wooden cabinets. After she has finished she finds that her screwdriver is magnetized. Suggest why.

4 The student uses speakers marked 'Maximum power 30 W'. He connects them to a stereo system marked 'Power output 50 W per channel'. Suggest what might happen if he turns the volume up to its maximum level. Explain your answer.

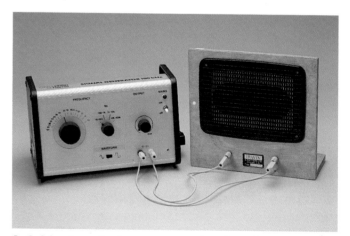

In the laboratory a signal generator can produce alternating currents at variable frequency. It can drive a loudspeaker to give sounds at different pitches.

Electromagnetic induction

We have seen that motion can be produced when a current flows in a magnetic field. It is possible to show that a current is produced when a wire is moved through a magnetic field. This is the opposite of the motor effect. It is called the **dynamo effect**.

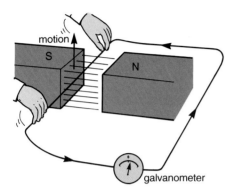

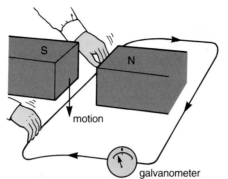

*As the wire is moved **through** the field, a current flows in the circuit.*

If the wire is moved in the opposite direction, the current reverses.

If the wire is moved parallel to the field lines so that it does not cut them, no current flows.

The size of the current can be increased by:

- moving the wire faster
- using a stronger magnetic field
- increasing the length of wire in the field by looping it around the magnetic poles.

A current can also be generated (**induced**) by moving a magnet towards or away from a coil of wire. The current is only induced when the magnet is moving. This is when the number of field lines linking with the coil is changing.

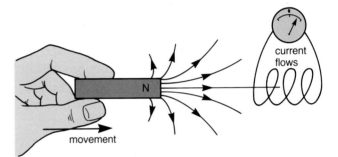

As the magnet is moved, the number of field lines linking with the coil changes. This induces a current in the coil.

The size of the current can be increased by:

- moving the magnet faster
- using a stronger magnet
- using more turns of wire in the coil.

Using electromagnetic induction

The moving-coil microphone. We have seen that a loudspeaker uses the motor effect to turn electrical signals into sound. The moving-coil microphone uses the dynamo effect to turn sound waves into an electrical signal.

The diagram shows the parts of a moving coil microphone. The sound waves make the thin diaphragm vibrate. This makes the coil move backwards and forwards in the magnetic field causing a small alternating current. This can be amplified to drive a loudspeaker, or the signal can be recorded on tape.

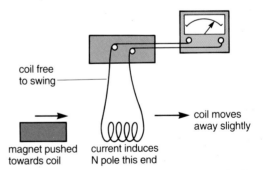

Lenz's law: the induced current flows in a direction to oppose the change producing it (in this case the motion of the magnet).

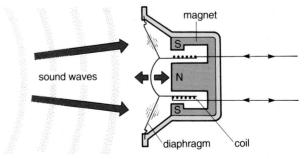

The moving-coil microphone

Storing information using magnetism

Magnetism has become very important in the modern world for storing information. It is used to record sound on audio tape, pictures on video tape, and data on computer diskettes. Credit cards and cash dispenser cards have a magnetic strip which stores details of the cardholder's bank account.

Computer disk drives, video recorders, and cassette players are designed for their own special purposes, but they record and play back using the same principles. We can understand these by studying how sound is recorded on magnetic tape.

Recording sound

Audio cassettes use plastic tape coated with a fine powder of magnetic material. This is mainly iron oxide, Fe_2O_3, sometimes mixed with other metal oxides to give better results.

To record on a blank cassette, the sound is turned into an electrical signal by a microphone. This signal is then sent to an electromagnet called a **recording head**. The signal varies the strength of the magnetic field in the narrow gap between the poles of the electromagnet. This magnetizes the particles in the coating of the tape as it is pulled past. The pattern of the magnetism then matches the signal from the microphone. Once the tape has passed the recording head the particles stay magnetized unless the tape is demagnetized or recorded over.

Playback

When a recorded audio cassette is played, a motor pulls the tape past a **playback head** which is just like the recording head. In fact, most cassette players use the same head for both jobs. This time the varying magnetic field of the particles in the tape induces a small current in the wires around the head. The signal is amplified and then fed into a loudspeaker where it is turned into sound which matches the original.

Activities

1   Conduct a survey at home or at school to investigate how common magnetic recording is. Find the answers to the following questions:
   a)   How many audio cassettes are there at home/school?
   b)   How many cassette players are there?

These can all be used to store information magnetically.

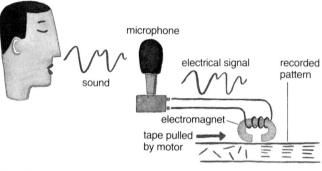

Recording on audio tape

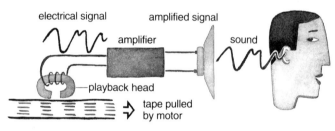

Playback of a recording on audio tape

   c)   Is there a video recorder?
   d)   How many video cassettes are there? What is their total playing time?
   e)   Is there a computer?
   f)   Does the computer use tape or diskettes?
   g)   How many tapes or diskettes are there at home/school?
   h)   On average, how many credit cards or other cards with magnetic recording strips does an adult carry?

2   A typical computer diskette can store around a megabyte of information. (One megabyte means 1 048 576 bytes – a byte can store one character. A character is a letter, a number, a punctuation mark, or even a space!) Calculate roughly how many pages of typing could be stored on a diskette.

Questions

1 A student has a magnetic compass. He also has three metal bars painted to look the same. One is copper, one is unmagnetized iron, and the other is a permanent magnet. Describe how he can find out which bar is the magnet.

2 The diagram shows a piece of iron held by attraction to a magnet.

a) Copy the diagram. Mark on the iron where the induced N and S poles are.
b) One theory of magnetism uses the idea that iron contains tiny 'molecular magnets' which can line up in magnetic fields. Use this theory to explain, with diagrams, how an unmagnetized iron bar is attracted to a magnet.

3
a) Describe briefly two ways of turning an unmagnetized steel rod into a permanent magnet.
b) Describe briefly two ways of demagnetizing a steel rod which has become magnetized.

4 A credit card has a magnetic strip on the back.
a) Using your knowledge of tape recording, suggest how information can be stored on the strip.
b) At a shop, an assistant slides the card through a machine that reads the information. Suggest how the machine might work.
c) A science teacher carries a purse containing her bank and credit cards in the pocket of her laboratory coat. One day, after teaching magnetism to Year 9, she goes to get money from an automatic cash dispenser. The machine will not accept her card! Suggest why.

5 The diagram shows a simple motor.

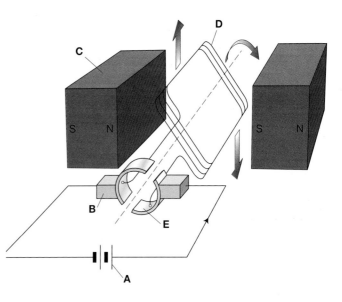

a) Match the following names with the labels A-E.
armature   brush   battery
magnet   coil
b) Which parts of the motor are likely to be made from:
i) copper   ii) carbon?

6 The diagram shows a reed switch that is 'normally closed'. When a magnet is nearby, the switch opens.

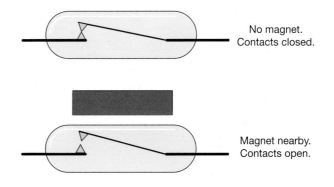

No magnet. Contacts closed.

Magnet nearby. Contacts open.

Design an alarm system, using this switch, which will sound an alarm when a door is opened.

Don't forget to include: a power supply (battery), the reed switch, a magnet, a bell or siren.

Explain how your alarm works.

8 | The solar system

How did the universe begin?
What is the solar system?
What causes days, months, and years?
Why do we have seasons?
Why are there tides?
How do people get into space?

The universe contains everything that exists. We don't know how big the universe is, or even if there is a limit to its size. Planet Earth is just a tiny part of the universe. It is part of a galaxy called the **Milky Way**. Astronomers once thought that the Milky Way was the only galaxy. Today, however, we know that our galaxy is only one of many star systems scattered throughout the universe. Each galaxy contains millions of stars together with clouds of dust and gases.

The arrow shows the position of the Earth in the Milky Way. There are thousands and thousands of stars in the Milky Way. These stars give a milky appearance to the night sky, hence the name.

The Horse Head nebula is a cloud of dust and gases hiding stars in the constellation of Orion in the Milky Way. It is about 5 light years across. (One light year is the distance travelled in one year by light travelling at 186,000 miles per second.) This is a dark nebula. Other nebulae consisting of glowing patches of gas are much brighter.

Galaxies are very far apart. The nearest large galaxy to the Milky Way is called **Andromeda**. Andromeda is two million light years away. This means that the light we see from Andromeda has taken two million years to reach us. We are seeing it as it was two million years ago – before there were humans on Earth.

When we look through a telescope into space we are looking at something not only very far away but also back in time. Some of the more distant galaxies that have been discovered are thousands of millions of light years away. Astronomers believe that there are many more galaxies further out into space that can't be seen.

Questions

1 What is a galaxy? What galaxy does the Earth belong to? How does it get its name?

2 What is a nebula? Suggest how the Horse Head nebula got its name.

3 Explain what is meant by a light year. How far is a light year in miles?

4 How big is the universe? How big is the planet Earth in comparison?

The planets of our solar system

The Earth is one of at least nine planets which travel around the Sun. The planets follow elliptical paths or orbits so their distance from the Sun is always changing. Moons orbit some of the planets. Like the Earth, the planets rotate on their axes although they rotate at different speeds. Only Earth appears to be capable of supporting life as we know it.

This diagram shows the planets in order of their distance from the Sun.

Planet facts: Earth
Distance from the Sun: 149M km
Diameter: 12 800 km
Time for one rotation: 23 h 56 min
Time to orbit the Sun: 365.25 days
Surface temperature: −90°C to +60°C
Atmosphere: water vapour, nitrogen, oxygen
Number of moons: 1

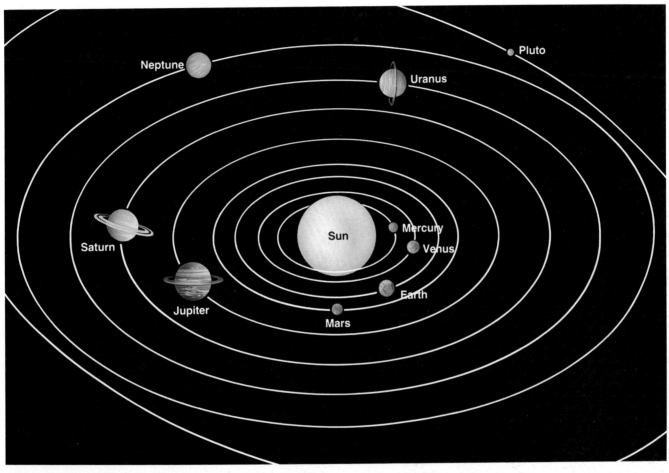

Planets of the solar system

Some astronomers have suggested that another planet may lie far beyond the orbit of Pluto. They have come to this idea after studying the paths of comets, including Halley's comet. As comets pass beyond Pluto and out of our solar system, they appear to be influenced by other gravitational fields.

All the planets and other bodies revolving around the Sun are held in orbit by the force of gravity. The Sun is by far the biggest body in our solar system. It therefore exerts a gravitational force that is strong enough to hold the largest and most distant planets.

Activities

1   Think of an easy way to remember the order of planets in our solar system. You could try making up a sentence with words beginning with the initial letter of each planet. On the other hand, you may think of some other way!

Days, months, and years

The Earth is constantly spinning. It rotates around an axis through the North and South Poles. The time taken for one complete rotation of the Earth is 24 hours or one day. If you watch the Sun at different times in the day you will see that it appears to move from east to west. In fact this motion is due to the Earth spinning on its axis.

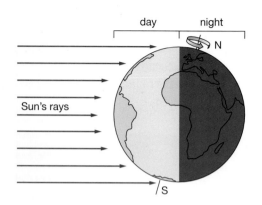

When the part of Earth on which you live is facing the Sun it is daytime. Night-time falls when your part of the Earth faces away from the Sun, towards where there is no light.

The Moon revolves around the Earth once every 27.3 days. This is a **lunar month**. When the side lit by the Sun faces the Earth we see a **full Moon**. Sometimes we see no Moon at all. This is when the Moon is on the side of Earth nearest to the Sun. This is called a **new Moon**. Between these two positions we see only a part of the Moon. These sections of reflecting surfaces are called the **phases of the Moon**.

Why do we see the Moon differently at certain times of the month?

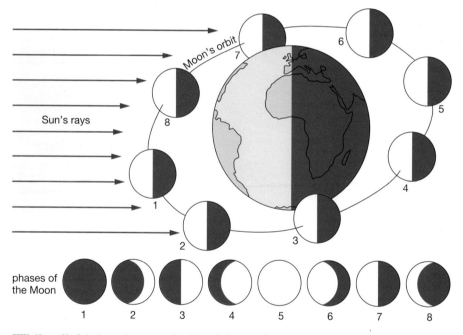

Whilst all this is going on, the Earth is revolving around the Sun. One complete orbit takes about 365.25 days or **one year**. Obviously we can't have a quarter of a day at the end of each calendar year. So the quarters are added together to produce an extra day every four years. Years that have the extra day are called **leap years**. The extra day is 29 February. A year has an extra day if its number divides exactly by four, e.g. 1992. If the year divides exactly by 100 it is not a leap year, e.g. 1900. On the other hand, if a year divides exactly by 400 it is a leap year, e.g. 2000. This correction means that three days are lost every 400 years. It is called the **Gregorian correction** and it keeps the Christian calendar in line with the movements of the Sun and the stars.

Questions

1 Which direction does the Earth spin in?

2 Why is it dark at night?

3 What is the difference between a full Moon and a new Moon?

4 What is **a**) a day **b**) a month **c**) a year?

5 Draw diagrams showing the eight phases of the Moon.

6 Why do we have leap years? Which of the following are leap years: 1596, 1600, 1700, 1760, 1800?

What year were you born? Was it a leap year?

The seasons

The Earth's axis is tilted at an angle of 23° to its orbit. During the year the Earth revolves around the Sun. This means that at certain times of the year the North and South Poles are tilted towards the Sun in turn. The part of the Earth which is tilted towards the Sun gets more light and is warmer. It has its **summer**. The part which is tilted away from the Sun gets less light and is colder. It has its **winter**.

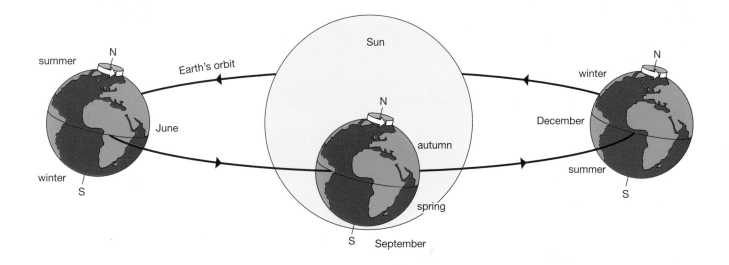

During spring and autumn in the UK, we get equal amounts of light because the Earth is tilted neither towards nor away from the Sun.

Activities

1 Hold a piece of plain white card vertically and shine a lighted torch or bicycle lamp onto it.

– Tilt the card slowly to an angle of about 45°.

How does **a)** the shape **b)** the brightness of the light change? Why is this?

– Now try the same exercise with a football. Set up your investigation like this:

Is the brightness of the light the same over the whole surface of the football?
If not, how does it differ?

– Mark the position of the equator on your football with a pencil.

– Hold the football at an angle of about 25°. Shine the torch on the football from four different positions around it like this:

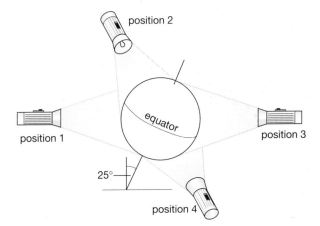

Describe the brightness of the upper and lower halves of the football with the torch in each of the four positions.

Why can Australians have Christmas dinner on the beach?

The Moon – the Earth's satellite

The Moon is the Earth's natural satellite. It orbits Earth in the same way as the Earth and the other planets orbit the Sun. It is our nearest neighbour in space and the only other part of our solar system to have been visited by humans.

The Moon lies 384 000 km from the Earth and has a diameter of about 3500 km. It is much less dense than Earth and has only one-sixth of Earth's gravity. It has no atmosphere and no signs of life. The Moon rotates very slowly. It rotates once in the same time as it takes to complete one orbit of Earth. This means that the Moon always keeps the same side facing the Earth. The dark side can only be seen from space. This slow spin speed also means that Moon days and Moon nights last for 14 Earth days. During a Moon day, temperatures rise to as much as 120 °C. At night, however, temperatures may fall to –150 °C or lower. The surface of the Moon is dry, hard, and covered in loose dust. It is pitted with many large impact craters. These **craters** are caused by **meteorites** as they collide with the Moon. Some craters are over 100 km across.

Lunar eclipse

A lunar eclipse happens when the Earth comes between the Moon and the Sun. In most lunar eclipses we can see the shadow of the Earth slowly moving across the face of the Moon.

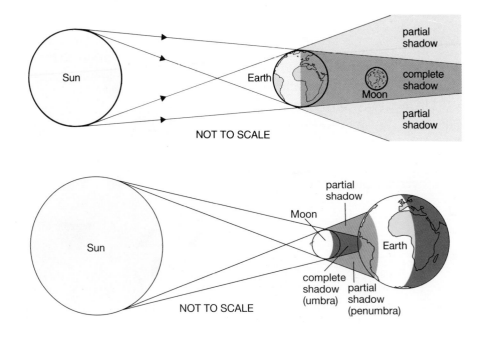

Solar eclipses

A solar eclipse is caused when the Moon, in its orbit around the Earth, comes between the Earth and the Sun. Light from the Sun is hidden and the Moon appears to us as a black disc surrounded by the Sun's bright chromosphere and corona.

A star called the Sun

You probably think of stars as tiny specks of light twinkling in the sky billions of miles away from Earth. There is one star, however, that we see every day quite close to Earth. This star is the **Sun**. The Sun is the star of our solar system.

The Sun is an enormous body. It has a mass of about 330 000 times that of Earth and is about 1 384 000 km in diameter. The distance between Earth and the Sun is about 149 million kilometres. This is a relatively short distance compared to the vast expanse of space. It is because the Sun is so near that it appears so large. In fact the Sun is small in comparison to other stars. Our next nearest star, **Alpha Centauri**, is much bigger but looks tiny because it is further away.

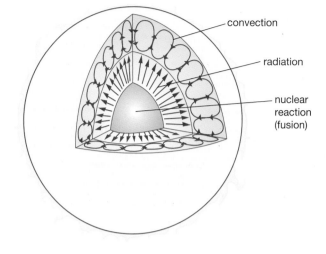

The Sun - a thermonuclear reactor.

Scientists think the Sun was formed from gas and dust over 5000 million years ago. As gases collected together, the core became compressed, temperatures rose, and hydrogen atoms fused to form helium atoms. As helium atoms form, energy in the form of heat and light is released. This is a nuclear fusion reaction. Large numbers of helium atoms form every second and the heat is intense. Temperatures in the centre of the Sun are estimated at over 14 000 000 °C. The surface temperature is about 6000 °C.

How long will the Sun live?

When the hydrogen in the Sun runs out nuclear fusion will stop. There will be a fall in pressure at the centre of the Sun and the star will collapse. This sudden collapse will cause the temperature at the Sun's centre to rise above 100 000 000 °C. At such high temperatures helium atoms will fuse to make heavier elements. The Sun will get bigger and bigger forming a *red giant*. This red giant will engulf Mercury and burn up the Earth before finally collapsing again to finish its life as a tiny smouldering *white dwarf* star.

Don't worry – scientists estimate that it will be another 5000 million years before the Sun turns into a red giant!

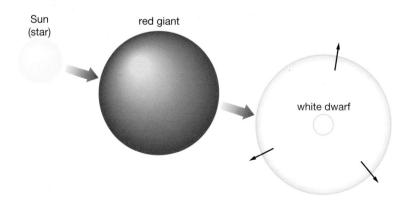

Death of a star.

Sunspots are dark patches on the surface of the Sun. They appear mainly in pairs or in small clusters in areas where the Sun's surface has cooled to about 4000 °C.

Charged particles are shot out of sunspots far into space. Sometimes these reach the Earth's atmosphere and produce brilliant light displays called **aurorae**. The Northern Lights are an example of an aurora. Unfortunately the particles also cause interference to radio and television broadcasts. Scientists have found that sunspots become more frequent every 11 years or so. They cannot yet explain why this pattern occurs.

Activities

1   Find out how far Alpha Centauri is from the Earth in light years. How far away is the Sun in light minutes?

2   Find out about the death of stars which are much more massive than our Sun. Hint: look for the words 'supernova', 'neutron star', 'black hole'.

Gravity – keeping the planets in orbit

The force of gravity

How often have you dropped a plate when doing the washing up?
Everyone knows that objects fall when they are dropped. This
downward motion is due to the **gravitational force**, pulling the object
towards the centre of the Earth. Sir Isaac Newton came to the
conclusion that gravitational forces exist between **all** bodies; not only
are objects attracted to the Earth, but they also attract each other.
Usually we do not notice the tiny forces between small objects.
However, the larger the objects become, the greater the gravitational
forces between them. That is why we notice the pull of the Earth's
gravitational field on our bodies.

Newton's law of gravitation tells us:

- The size of the gravitational force depends on the **masses** of the
  two objects attracting each other. The bigger the masses, the greater
  the forces due to gravity.

- The size of the gravitational force depends on the **distance** between
  the two objects. As the distance increases, the forces due to gravity
  get smaller. However, gravity can act over very large distances.

Gravity causes this apple to fall. It also keeps the planets in their orbits.

Gravity and orbits

The planets of the solar system are in **orbit** around the Sun. The
planets are held in orbit by the Sun's gravitational pull. They keep
moving at very high speeds through space because there is very little
friction to slow them down.

The orbits of the planets are shaped like **ellipses**. The Earth's elliptical
orbit is almost circular, with the Sun at the centre. The gravitational
pull of the Sun is the **centripetal force** which holds the Earth on its
circular path and prevents it from flying out into space. (This is just
like the way the Earth's gravitational pull holds our Moon in its
circular orbit around us.)

Comets are bodies of rock and ice that orbit the Sun. They are
attracted by its gravitational field. Some comets can be seen regularly
because they are held in closed, elliptical orbits. For example, Halley's
comet is seen about every 76 years. Other comets move too quickly to
be held by the Sun's gravitational field. They swing around the Sun
and then shoot out of the solar system, never to be seen again.

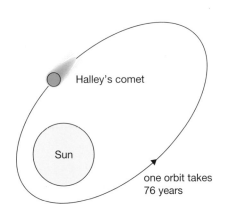

Planets, moons and comets are all kept in orbit by gravity.

Question

1 Draw a diagram showing the orbit of the Earth
around the Sun, and the Moon around the Earth.
On your diagram, mark the direction of the forces
that keep:
  (i) the Earth in orbit,
  (ii) the Moon in orbit.

2 a) Halley's comet was last seen in 1986.
Approximately when will you be able to see
it again?
b) The Bayeux tapestry shows the Battle of
Hastings in 1066. The pictures include a comet
in the sky. Prove that this was Halley's comet.

Bullets, missiles, and satellites

All objects accelerate when they fall straight downwards, but what happens if they are already moving along horizontally? The diagram shows a ball rolling along a table at a steady speed. When it reaches the edge of the table it keeps moving forwards at the same speed but also starts to accelerate downwards. The forwards and downwards motions together give a special curved shape called a **parabola**.

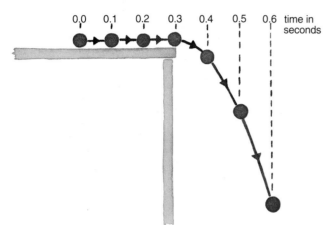

Horizontal motion + vertical acceleration gives movement in a parabola.

Activities

1 If the downwards acceleration is only due to gravity then the sideways speed should not affect time taken for the object to fall to the ground.

Take two coins, one in each hand, and stand on a chair. Hold your hands out in front of you at the same height. Drop them at exactly the same time. You should hear them hit the floor at the same time. Repeat the exercise but this time drop one coin straight down and throw the other one out sideways at the same time. This takes good co-ordination but after practice you should be able to do it. No matter how fast you throw the coin out sideways (provided it is thrown horizontally) the two coins will always hit the floor at the same time.

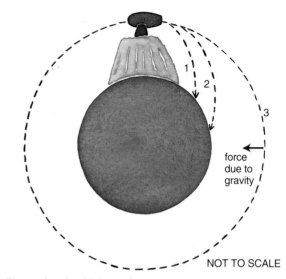

Satellites are kept in orbit by gravity.

The diagram above shows a gun at the top of a mountain. The curved surface of the Earth is greatly exaggerated.

Path 1 shows the parabola followed by a shell fired horizontally from the gun.

Path 2 shows what would happen if the shell left the gun at a greater speed. It would obviously travel further before it hit the Earth.

Path 3 shows a shell fired at an even greater speed. This one is travelling at so great a speed that it never reaches the ground. It keeps going around the Earth. It is a **satellite**!

Real satellites are launched by rockets. It is the pull of gravity towards the centre of the Earth which keeps them in orbit. (This force towards the centre is called **the centripetal force**.)

This satellite is constantly falling under gravity in a circular orbit around the Earth.

Satellites

Artificial satellites

The Moon is a natural satellite of our planet. However, there are hundreds of man-made objects in orbit around the Earth. These are **satellites** that have been launched from rockets or the American space shuttle. They are held in orbit by the gravitational force of the Earth.

The speed of a satellite depends on its height above the Earth. Satellites in low orbits travel faster than those in high orbits. For example, a satellite at 300 km, just above the atmosphere, orbits the Earth in 90 minutes. A satellite at a height of 36 000 km takes 24 hours to complete one orbit.

Satellites can be used for many things including:

- Surveying and mapping the planet.

- Investigating changes in the oceans, on the land, and in the atmosphere.

- Observing weather systems to forecast storms etc.

- Relaying communications from place to place.

- Gathering information on other countries ('spy satellites').

- Observing outer space from outside the Earth's atmosphere, e.g. Hubble telescope.

Geostationary satellites

A satellite that is 36 000 km above the Earth completes one orbit in 24 hours. This is the same time that the Earth takes to turn once on its axis. As a result, the satellite is always above the same place on the Earth's surface. It is as though it is not moving! Such **geostationary satellites** are very useful for sending information from one place to another. Messages are sent to the satellite using microwaves. The signal can carry TV programmes, telephone messages, and computer data. Satellite dishes (antennae) on the ground can be aimed at the satellite to receive signals.

Image from a weather satellite

Low, polar orbit satellites

Satellites can be placed in low orbits which pass over the North and South Poles. In 24 hours, the satellite makes about 16 orbits. Each time, it 'sees' a different part of the Earth because the planet is turning. The satellite can therefore build up a picture of the whole of the Earth's surface. This is very useful for monitoring the weather.

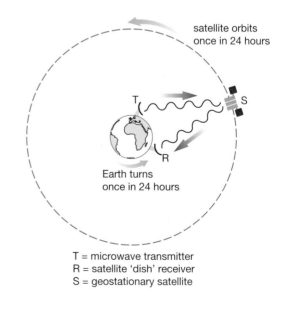

satellite orbits
once in 24 hours

Earth turns
once in 24 hours

T = microwave transmitter
R = satellite 'dish' receiver
S = geostationary satellite

1 Explain the following using diagrams:
a) Day and night are always of equal length at the Equator.
b) Day and night are of equal length twice a year in the UK.
c) At the North Pole it doesn't get dark, even at night, for a few weeks in June.
d) On December 21st it is midwinter in the UK but midsummer in Australia.

2 The diagram shows (not to scale) the orbits of the Earth and Halley's comet around the Sun. Copy the diagram and then use it to answer these questions:
a) On the diagram, draw arrows to show the direction of the Sun's gravitational pull on (i) the Earth, (ii) Halley's comet.
b) Explain why we can see Halley's comet every 76 years.

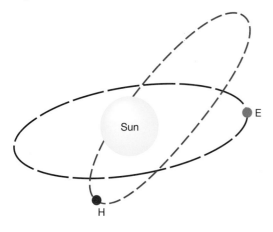

3
a) Give two uses for geostationary satellites.
b) Give two uses for low polar orbit satellites.
c) Suggest one reason why the Hubble space telescope gives better pictures than telescopes on Earth.
d) Write two paragraphs about how satellites affect your daily life. (Hint: think about information, communication, entertainment.)

4 The table gives information about four of the planets in our solar system.

planet	distance from the Sun	diameter	time to orbit Sun	surface temperature	atmosphere
Jupiter	780 Mkm	143 000 km	11.9 years	-150 °C	hydrogen/helium
Pluto	5900 Mkm	4000 km	248 years	-250 °C	unknown
Mars	228 Mkm	7000 km	1.9 years	-80 to +40 °C	carbon dioxide/nitrogen/oxygen
Mercury	57 Mkm	4800 km	88 days	-200 to +400 °C	very little

Use this information to answer the following:
a) Which is i) the largest ii) the smallest planet?
b) Which of the planets has i) the shortest ii) the longest year?
c) Which planet is furthest from the Sun?
d) Which planet has the greatest temperature range?
e) Some scientists have suggested that there is life on Mars. Give one reason why i) they could be right ii) they could be wrong.

5
a) What is an eclipse?
b) Draw diagrams to show the difference between a lunar and a solar eclipse.
c) Explain why the Sun appears as a black disc surrounded by a halo of bright light during a solar eclipse.
d) Why are total solar eclipses so rare?

6 Design an experiment to show that when a ball rolls off the end of a flat table, the path it follows as it falls is a parabola.

Your experiment should allow you to repeat your observations. How will you make sure that you can control the speed and direction of the ball? How will you observe and/or record the path of the ball as it falls?

What is inside the Earth?
How do we know?
How are rocks made and destroyed?
What causes earthquakes?
How is our planet changing?

Scientists who study rocks are called **geologists**. They get information about the structure of the Earth in four main ways:

- Studying rocks on the Earth's surface.

- Studying volcanoes and their products.

- Studying earthquakes and vibrations.

- Drilling deep into the Earth for rock samples.

Using all these methods, we have built up this picture of the inside of our planet.

The Earth is thought to be made up of three main layers:

- The **core** has two parts: a solid inner core consisting of a mixture of nickel and iron, and an outer core made of molten iron with some other elements. The temperature in the core is between 3700 °C and 4500 °C!

- The **mantle** is a little more complex. Near the core the rocks are made mainly of iron and magnesium silicates. Nearer to the surface the mantle is composed of igneous rocks, mainly peridotite. Mantle temperatures are between 1000 °C and 3700 °C.

- The **crust** is the thin layer of rocks directly under our feet. It contains rocks of lower density such as basalt and granite. Temperatures are very much cooler than those found deeper inside the Earth.

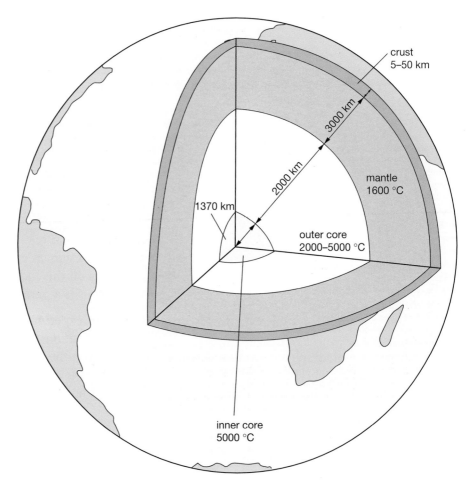

The structure of the Earth.

crust
5–50 km

3000 km

mantle
1600 °C

2000 km

1370 km

outer core
2000–5000 °C

inner core
5000 °C

How old is the Earth?

For many generations people have tried to work out the age of the Earth. Parts of its surface are extremely old – up to 4500 million years! Try to imagine what that means.

To help us to appreciate the enormous timescales involved in the evolution of the Earth, scientists have constructed the chart shown opposite. This chart is often referred to as the **stratigraphic column** for the Earth. It is made by drawing blocks to represent rocks of known ages on top of one another. The oldest are at the bottom and the youngest are at the top.

The whole of Earth's history is divided up into four major divisions called **eras**. Each era is further subdivided into **periods** or **epochs**. Rocks formed in these periods are named accordingly, for example, rocks between about 500 and 570 million years old belong to the Cambrian period.

Measuring the age of rocks

Fossils are the remains of plants and animals that lived millions of years ago which have become 'turned into stone' or fossilized. We can compare the age of rocks by comparing the fossils found in them. For example, rocks that contain fossils of birds are younger than rocks that contain primitive fish, because birds evolved after the first fish. The oldest rocks do not contain fossils because life only appeared on Earth about 500 million years ago.

Fossils can't tell us the age of a particular rock. Fortunately, rocks that contain radioactive elements such as uranium have a built-in 'clock'. As the uranium gives out radiation it steadily changes into other elements. Finally, lead is produced. By measuring the relative amounts of uranium and lead in a rock, and by knowing how long uranium takes to decay, we can work out the age of the rock. This is called **radiometric dating**.

Activities

1   Copy and complete the table below using the information from the stratigraphic column.

rock	location	age	era	period
		(million yrs)		
granite	Peterhead, Scotland	385		
basalt	Auvergne, France	10		
peridotite	Ivrea, Italy	70		
sandstone	Leeds, England	300		
limestone	Derbyshire, England	320		

2   Use a geological map in an atlas to find the age of the rocks near your home. What period do they date from?

era	period	millions of years ago
Cenozoic	Quaternary	2
Cenozoic	Tertiary	65
Mesozoic	Cretaceous	145
Mesozoic	Jurassic	215
Mesozoic	Triassic	250
Palaeozoic	Permian	285
Palaeozoic	Carboniferous	360
Palaeozoic	Devonian	410
Palaeozoic	Silurian	440
Palaeozoic	Ordovician	505
Palaeozoic	Cambrian	570
Precambrian		4600

The geological eras.

Questions

1   Roughly how old is the Earth?

2   Fossils of fish are found in the Ordovician period, but not in earlier rocks. Roughly how long ago did fish appear on the Earth?

3   Fossils of dinosaurs are found in Cretaceous rocks but not in Tertiary rocks. Roughly how long ago did dinosaurs become extinct?

4   Coal deposits are from the Carboniferous period. Roughly how old is a lump of coal?

5   Explain why rocks containing radioactive elements can be dated more accurately than those that do not.

Rocks and minerals

Rocks are made of mineral particles cemented together or crystallized into a large mass.

Minerals occur naturally in the Earth's crust. They usually have definite chemical compositions and physical structures. Because their atoms are well ordered, minerals often appear as **crystals**.

Some minerals have very attractive colours and crystal shapes and are used for decoration. Rubies, diamonds, sapphires, topaz and emeralds are examples. Other minerals are used as a source of metals. Most minerals are mixtures (or **compounds**) of several elements, for example galena is a mineral made from atoms of lead and sulphur.

Notice how the arrangement of lead and sulphur atoms produces the cube-shaped crystals of galena. You can sometimes see crystals in rock formations if you look carefully. Crystals of one mineral always form similar shapes and the angles between the faces are always the same. So, although we cannot see individual atoms inside minerals we are able to get an idea of their arrangement by looking at the shape of the crystals they produce.

If you look at the bar graph on the right you will notice that the two most abundant elements in the Earth's crust are oxygen and silicon. It is therefore no great surprise to learn that the most common rock-forming minerals are metal **silicates**. These compounds contain a metal, oxygen and silicon joined together. Granite, sandstone and slate are all silicate rocks, though there are a great many more. All silicates are resistant to chemical change. That is why they are often used in the building industry.

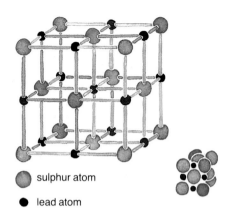

○ sulphur atom

● lead atom

Crystal structure of galena

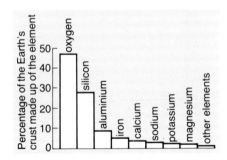

Crystals of galena

The main elements in the Earth's crust

Feldspar

Mica

Quartz

Feldspar
Pink or grey crystals: resistant to heat, water, and chemical attack: used in making ceramics.
Quartz
A crystalline form of silicon dioxide: resistant to heat and chemical attack: used in making pottery and glass.
Mica
Flat, transparent crystals: high melting point and good electrical insulator: used as an insulator in, for example, electric irons.

Questions

1 What is the difference between a rock and a mineral?

2 How do crystals help scientists understand the arrangement of atoms in minerals?

3 What are metal silicates?

4 What do all silicates have in common?

5 Glass contains silicates. Why is glass apparatus used in laboratory experiments?

The rock cycle: igneous rocks

Rocks are being made all around us now. This may be hard to believe since rocks always seem to be static things that never change. However, if we lived for ten thousand years we would be able to observe the ways in which one rock is gradually produced from another. This is part of **the rock cycle**.

Igneous rocks form the starting point in the rock cycle. Igneous rocks are sometimes called volcanic rocks because they are produced by the solidification on the Earth's surface of molten rock from volcanoes.

The molten rock or **magma** comes from the mantle of the Earth. Most volcanic rocks are crystalline. The size of the crystals depends upon how long the magma takes to cool down. Slow cooling gives big crystals and rapid cooling gives small crystals. All the material from which other rocks have been made originally came from igneous rocks.

The following diagram tells you more about volcanoes and igneous rocks.

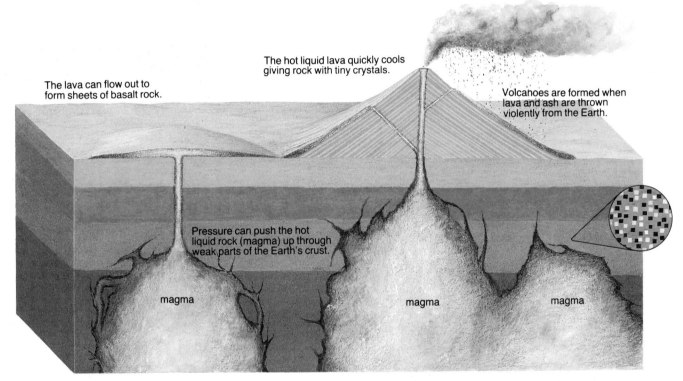

The lava can flow out to form sheets of basalt rock.

The hot liquid lava quickly cools giving rock with tiny crystals.

Volcanoes are formed when lava and ash are thrown violently from the Earth.

Pressure can push the hot liquid rock (magma) up through weak parts of the Earth's crust.

magma   magma   magma

Formation of igneous rocks

Questions

1 *Ignis* is the latin word for 'fire'. Why do you think volcanic rocks are called 'igneous'?

2 What is magma? Where is it formed?

3 Why are most igneous rocks crystalline?

4 Suggest why granite contains larger crystals than basalt.

5 Why is diamond so hard?

6 Why does pumice float?

Diamond *(carbon), the hardest natural substance, is formed in volcanic rock where temperature and pressure are very high.*

Bubbles of gas are often released from molten lava making it frothy. When this solidifies a rock called **pumice** *is formed – it floats.*

The rock cycle: metamorphic rocks

Metamorphism means 'change of form'. Many sedimentary and igneous rocks have been subjected to mechanical forces, squeezing and pushing, and to different conditions of temperature and pressure since they were formed. These processes produce a new group of rocks called **metamorphic rocks**.

For example, rock can be changed when very hot magma is pushed up into it. Where the magma pushes into other rocks, it is called an **intrusion**. The size of the intrusion is important. Small intrusions will not heat up the surrounding rock as much as large ones. The diagram shows how the metamorphic rocks marble and quartzite are made as a result of a magma intrusion into bands of sedimentary limestone and sandstone. Rather like a cake being baked, the end product is very different to the original mixture.

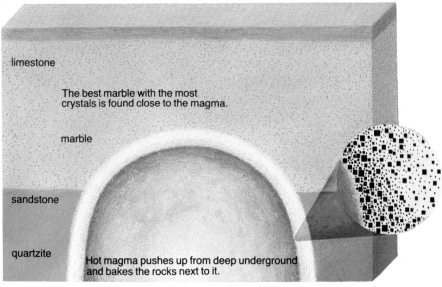

limestone

The best marble with the most crystals is found close to the magma.

marble

sandstone

quartzite

Hot magma pushes up from deep underground and bakes the rocks next to it.

Making metamorphic rocks

Metamorphic rocks are extemely hard (like burnt cakes!) and usually have a spotty appearance due to the formation of new minerals inside them. The type of rock formed depends upon the area of contact between the magma intrusion and the surrounding rock. The best marble is formed immediately next to the magma.

Regional metamorphism affects very large masses of rock and is usually associated with mountain building. Most of the continents of the Earth are regionally metamorphosed rocks. Huge movements of the Earth subjected rocks to great pressure and high temperatures. This formed new rocks.

Splitting slate

Slate is a dull grey rock formed when sedimentary mudstone was compressed deep underground. Mudstone grains grew into flaky crystals which were arranged in parallel layers. This is why slate splits easily into flat sheets. These have been used for many years in the building industry as roofing material though today they are expensive to produce and have mostly been replaced by manufactured clay or cement tiles.

Questions

1 What is metamorphic rock?

2 Explain how marble is made.

3 Why are some statues made from marble and not limestone?

4 Explain why very old marble statues, like those in Greece, are not quite like they were when they were made.
(*Hint*: remember that rain water is slightly acid.)

5 How was slate made?

Marble statues, badly affected by air pollution

The rock cycle: sedimentary rocks

Once igneous rocks are exposed to the atmosphere on the surface of the Earth, they start to be broken down. The silicate minerals of the igneous rock are attacked by chemical and physical processes that lead to their destruction. This is known as **weathering**. The products of the weathering action accumulate to form **sedimentary rocks**. Sandstone, clay, limestone and chalk are sedimentary rocks.

There are two main types of weathering:

Physical weathering

Rocks can be worn away or **eroded** by the action of wind but perhaps the best example of physical weathering is frost shattering. Water seeps into cracks in the rock and then freezes. As it turns to ice it expands and forces the rock to split. Large boulders fall and shatter to form **scree** at the foot of mountain slopes. You can see the effect of frost action on road surfaces after a severe winter.

Scree

Chemical weathering

Scree fragments and exposed rock faces are open to attack by rain-water. Rain-water absorbs carbon dioxide from the air making it slightly acidic. Chemical reactions take place between the water and the rock minerals causing them to crumble and possibly be dissolved and carried away.

Some minerals such as quartz are not affected by chemical weathering whereas others like feldspar are broken down to clay minerals. In Cornwall the minerals in the granite have been broken down to form china clay – the basis of the North Staffordshire pottery industry.

Transporting the weathered material

Weathered rock fragments are washed into rivers.

Rivers carry rock fragments to the sea.

Rock fragments are deposited as sand and gravel in the sea.

Formation of sedimentary rocks

Over millions of years sediment will pile up forcing water out of the lower layers and compacting them together, eventually forming rock. The size and origin of the sediment particles will determine the type of sedimentary rock that is produced. Sandstone for example is formed from compacted sand grains. Limestone contains a large proportion of organic material such as calcium carbonate from the shells and skeletons of marine creatures.

Questions

1   Explain why a cold winter can cause damage to road surfaces.

2   Describe how a mountain is eroded.

3   What is sediment? Why do the mouths of rivers sometimes need to be cleared by dredgers?

4   Beach sand contains very small, smooth sand grains of different colours. How do you explain these facts?

And so the rock cycle is complete

When you look at a mountain or a large cliff face it is easy to think that rocks are permanent and will never change. However, it is important to realize that rocks play a temporary part in the evolution of our planet. Igneous rocks are weathered and eroded. The debris is transported then dumped to eventually become sedimentary rock. This may be buried deeply and changed by heat and pressure (metamorphism) and then be lifted to form a mountain range only to be eroded again! The rock cycle goes on and on . . .

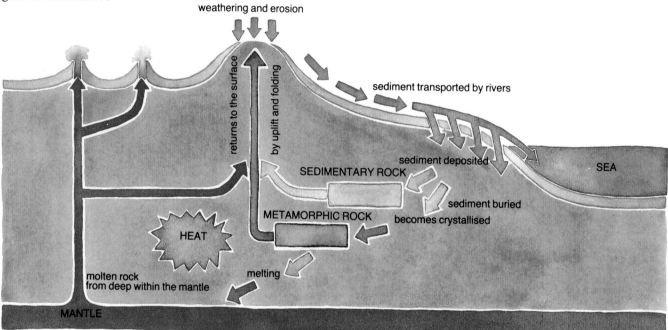

The rock cycle

'The present is the key to the past'

In the late eighteenth century James Hutton put forward one of the most important ideas in earth science. It was called **uniformitarianism**.

Hutton believed that we can understand the geological history of the Earth surface by studying the processes that we can see happening today – the rock cycle!

Questions

1 Explain why the rock cycle is called a **cycle**.

2 In theory, material from the mantle could reach the surface and then be reburied until it became molten again.
    a) Describe briefly how this could happen.
    b) Roughly how long do you think the cycle would take?

3 Why is water important in the rock cycle?

4 'All mountains we see today were formed at the beginning of the Earth and will never change.'
Do you agree with this statement? Explain your answer.

Tectonic processes: what are they?

Volcanic rocks and sediments were originally laid down in horizontal layers or **strata**. However, if you look at rocks in quarries or cliff faces you may notice that the rocks are tilted, bent or fractured. They are no longer horizontal. These rocks have been deformed by mechanical forces or **tectonic processes**. (Tectonic comes from the Greek word for carpenter – someone who shapes wood and makes new structures).

Four things influence the way in which rock is deformed:

- the kind of rock it is, some are more plastic than others.
- the temperature – rock is more plastic at high temperatures.
- the force applied, whether it is a compression (push) or tension (pull).
- the length of time that the forces act.

You can model these effects by using pieces of Plasticine.

The greater the time that a force is applied the greater the change in shape of the rock layers. If rock is kept under a constant force it will continue to move or **creep**. Creep causes problems for engineers building large structures such as bridges.

A suspension bridge

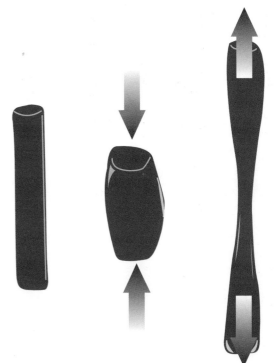

Plasticine models showing tectonic processes.

The middle 'rock' has been compressed. The forces have made it bulge.

The 'rock' on the right has been under tension. The forces have stretched it.

Questions

1 **a)** Explain why new layers of rock are usually horizontal.
 b) Why are the layers of rock in cliff faces often tilted or broken?

2 What is **a)** compression **b)** tension?

3 Describe, using diagrams, the effects that
 a) compression **b)** tension forces have on rock deformation.

4 List some examples of structures (e.g. bridges) that may be affected by 'creep'.

Joints and faults

Fractures, or breaks, in layers of rocks are often due to tension. They are usually found in igneous rocks. Hot volcanic rocks shrink as they cool. This sets up pulling forces in the rock causing it to break up into a clear pattern of fractures or **joints**.

Joints are very common in all kinds of rocks and are simply cracks in a piece of rock where it has split but where the pieces have not moved apart.

The Giant's Causeway in Antrim, Northern Ireland is a marvellous example of jointing. The basalt (an igneous rock) has cooled, shrunk and produced vertical joints. These outline perfect hexagonal columns.

The granite tors of Dartmoor are also the result of jointing, this time rectangular blocks are produced.

Faults are formed when movement takes place along a fracture line in a piece of rock. Because the rocks on one side of the fracture line move, they no longer line up with the rocks on the other side.

There are various kinds of faults. The most common is a **normal fault** like the one shown in the photograph below.

Giant's Causeway, County Antrim

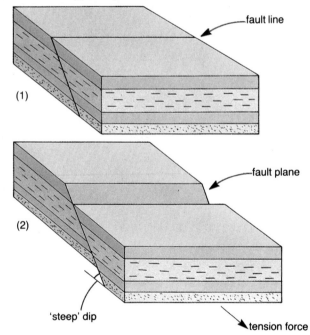

A normal fault. Movement takes place along a fault plane. The angle between the fault plane and the horizontal is called the dip.

A normal fault. The rocks on the right have moved down in relation to those on the left. You should be able to match up the layers on either side.

Questions

1 What is the difference between a *joint* and a *fault*?

2 Why are joints usually associated with igneous rocks?

3 Under what conditions would you expect joints to form in sedimentary rocks? (You may need to look back to page 121.)

4 Suggest how the tors on Dartmoor were formed.

5 Describe how the fault shown in the diagram above could have been formed.

Earthquakes

Faults and folding result in vertical movements of rock. Other types of fault, called tear faults, allow rocks to move horizontally on either side of a fracture.

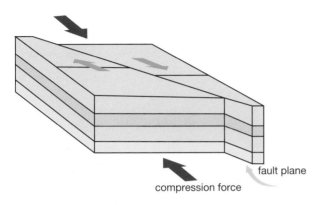

A sliding or tear fault.

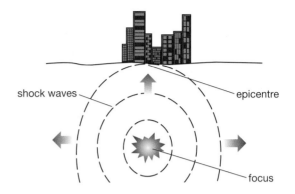

*Seismic waves are produced at a point called the focus, deep within the Earth. The point on the Earth's surface above the focus is called the **epicentre**.*

Unfortunately these movements are rarely smooth. As compression forces build up, a time is reached when something has to give. The rocks suddenly jerk past one another releasing energy as heat, sound and, more importantly, **shock** or **seismic waves**. We feel these as an earthquake.

Most major earthquakes appear in well-defined seismic zones called 'earthquake belts'. The seismic zones mark the edges of huge mobile pieces of the Earth's crust. These pieces are called **plates**.

The best known tear fault is the San Andreas fault in California. The last major earthquake in 1906 destroyed much of the city of San Francisco. Rocks slid 7 metres past each other over a distance of 300 kilometres. Compression forces have been accumulating ever since and experts are predicting another major earthquake soon!

In 1995, this earthquake in Kolbe, Japan killed over 6000 people and destroyed many buildings.

In 1990, an earthquake in Iran killed over 50 000 people. Most of these were killed when buildings collapsed.

Questions

1 What causes earthquakes?

2 **a)** Name three countries that lie in earthquake zones.
b) Why doesn't Britain have severe earthquakes?

3 Find out about the Richter scale for measuring the strength of earthquakes.

4 Even the smallest shock waves are recorded near the San Andreas fault. Why is this important for
a) geologists, **b)** people who live in San Francisco?

5

a) In many poorer countries, people are told to run out of their houses and into open space as soon as they feel the first tremors of an earthquake.
Suggest why this is good advice.

b) In California, people are advised to take cover (e.g. under tables, inside buildings) and **not** to run into the street.
Suggest why this is good advice.

Plate tectonics

The theory of plate tectonics suggests that the Earth's crust consists of large rigid plates of rock floating on the molten mantle. These plates are built up at ocean ridges and destroyed as they are forced beneath continents. It is believed that convection currents in the mantle cause the plates to move.

1 *Magma rises from the mantle by convection.*

2 *New ocean floor spreads outwards.*

3 *The floor of the Pacific Ocean is forced beneath South America. The ocean crust melts to form magma.*

4 *Volcano formed by rising magma.*

The Mid Atlantic Ridge – a constructive plate margin

Beneath the Atlantic Ocean, molten magma rises from the mantle below. This magma forms a ridge and creates new ocean floor. This in turn pushes the plates on either side away from each other and causes them to spread outwards. The rate of spreading can be calculated and is estimated to be up to 8 cm per year.

The west coast of South America – a destructive plate margin

For over a hundred million years South America has been moving slowly away from Africa and colliding with the floor of the Pacific Ocean. As the two plates meet the ocean floor is forced down into the mantle. The ocean floor gets hotter and melts to form magma. Magma rises up through the mantle and melts the continental crust above. Eventually magma may erupt through the surface to form a volcano.

Constructive and destructive plate margins

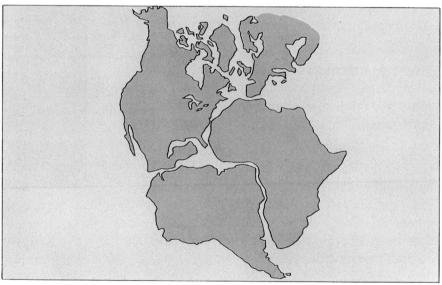

The planet Earth jigsaw!

Scientific evidence suggests therefore that the rocks of the ocean floor and the continents move slowly over the surface of the Earth. So it seems likely that the shape and positions of the continents have changed through time. There is a lot of support for this idea of **continental drift**. Earth scientists have been able to match up the rock types on either side of the Atlantic Ocean, some sedimentary rocks in South America and Africa even contain the same fossils. Even the present day shapes of the continents match, rather like a huge jig-saw puzzle.

Questions

1 Explain as simply as you can the theory of plate tectonics.

2 What happens at **a)** a constructive plate margin **b)** a destructive plate margin?

3 What is continental drift?

4 What evidence is there for the idea of continental drift?

5 Draw a diagram like the one above to show what might happen when two continents eventually collide.

Questions

1 Two students are talking.
Student A: "The Earth is a solid ball of rock."
Student B: "The Earth has a solid crust but the inside is completely full of molten rock."

a) What evidence would you use to show student A that the Earth is not solid?

b) Explain why the word 'crust' is a good description of the rocks near to the Earth's surface.

c) Draw a labelled diagram to show student B what geologists believe the Earth is like.

2 The deepest hole ever drilled is about 12 000 m (12 km) deep. The temperature at this depth is about 200 °C.

a) Give one reason why geologists drill such deep holes.

b) Suggest how we could make use of the hot rocks deep inside the Earth's crust.

3 The table below shows some of the rocks found in the United Kingdom.

place	rock	period
Edinburgh	basalt	Carboniferous
North Wales	slate	Cambrian
Yorkshire	coal	Carboniferous
Cotswolds	limestone	Jurassic

a) Granite is an **igneous** rock. Explain how it was formed.

b) Roughly how old are the mountains of North Wales?

c) Dinosaurs lived between 225 million and 65 million years ago.

i) Why don't we find dinosaur fossils in coal?

ii) Whereabouts in England might you find dinosaur fossils?

4 The diagram shows a house.

a) What type of rock is slate? Suggest why the builders chose slate for the roof.

b) What type of rock is clay?
Suggest why the builders chose clay bricks for the corners of the house.

c) Find out about the rock 'flint'. Suggest why the builders chose flint for the walls of the house.

5 The diagrams below show how our continents look now and how they might have looked 200 million years ago.

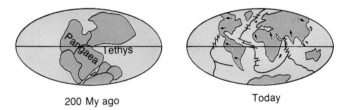

200 My ago   Today

a) Explain, using the theory of plate tectonics, how our continents have moved so far apart.

b) What evidence do scientists have for the theory of plate tectonics?

c) The distance between Africa and South America is roughly 7000 km. Estimate the average speed at which the continents are slowly moving apart.

Index